AGRICULTURE ISSUES AND POLICIES

THE 2014 FARM BILL

BIOENERGY PROVISIONS AND ISSUES

AGRICULTURE ISSUES AND POLICIES

Additional books in this series can be found on Nova's website
under the Series tab.

Additional e-books in this series can be found on Nova's website
under the e-book tab.

THE 2014 FARM BILL

BIOENERGY PROVISIONS AND ISSUES

WILMER COMBS
EDITOR

nova
publishers
New York

Library of Congress Cataloging-in-Publication Data

ISBN: 978-1-63321-432-3

Published by Nova Science Publishers, Inc. † New York

CONTENTS

PREFACE

This book focuses on those policies contained in the 2014 farm bill that support agriculture-based renewable energy, especially biofuels. The introductory sections of this book briefly describe how USDA bioenergy policies evolved and how they fit into the larger context of U.S. biofuels policy. Then, each of the bioenergy provisions of the 2014 farm bill are defined in terms of their function, goals, administration, funding, and implementation status. The book describes agriculture-based biofuels and the evolution of the U.S. biofuels sector with a focus on the role that federal policy has played in shaping its development. It highlights emerging issues that are critical to the biofuels sector and of relevance to Congress. Furthermore, this book provides a description of the Biomass Crop Assistance Program's main components—annual and establishment payments, matching payments, and project areas—as outlined in USDA's final rule, along with a discussion of program funding and implementation issues.

Chapter 1 – The farm bill is an omnibus, multi-year piece of authorizing legislation that governs an array of agricultural and food programs. Titles in the most recent farm bill encompassed farm commodity price and income supports, farm credit, trade, agricultural conservation, research, rural development, bioenergy, foreign food aid, and domestic nutrition assistance. Although agricultural policies sometimes are created and changed by freestanding legislation or as part of other major laws, the farm bill provides a predictable opportunity for policy makers to comprehensively and periodically address agricultural and food issues. The farm bill is renewed about every five years.

The Agricultural Act of 2014 (P.L. 113-79) is the most recent omnibus farm bill, and was enacted into law in February 2014. It succeeded the Food,

Conservation, and Energy Act of 2008 (P.L. 110-246). Provisions in the 2014 farm bill reshape the structure of farm commodity support, expand crop insurance coverage, consolidate conservation programs, reauthorize and revise nutrition assistance, and extend authority to appropriate funds for many U.S. Department of Agriculture (USDA) discretionary programs through FY2018.

Chapter 2 – Title IX, the Energy title of the 2014 farm bill (Agricultural Act of 2014; P.L. 113-79), contains authority for the bioenergy programs administered by the U.S. Department of Agriculture (USDA). USDA renewable energy programs have incentivized research, development, and adoption of renewable energy projects, including solar, wind, and anaerobic digesters. However, the primary focus of USDA renewable energy programs has been to promote U.S. biofuels production and use—including corn starch-based ethanol, cellulosic ethanol, and soybean-based biodiesel.

This report focuses on those policies contained in the 2014 farm bill that support agriculture-based renewable energy, especially biofuels. The introductory sections of this report briefly describe how USDA bioenergy policies evolved and how they fit into the larger context of U.S. biofuels policy. Then, each of the bioenergy provisions of the 2014 farm bill are defined in terms of their function, goals, administration, funding, and implementation status.

Chapter 3 – Since the late 1970s, U.S. policymakers at both the federal and state levels have authorized a variety of incentives, regulations, and programs to encourage the production and use of agriculture-based biofuels— i.e., any fuel produced from biological materials. Initially, federal biofuels policies were developed to help kick-start the biofuels industry during its early development, when neither production capacity nor a market for the finished product was widely available. Federal policy (e.g., tax credits, import tariffs, grants, loans, and loan guarantees) has played a key role in helping to close the price gap between biofuels and cheaper petroleum fuels. Now, as the industry has evolved, other policy goals (e.g., national energy security, climate change concerns, support for rural economies) are cited by proponents as justification for continuing or enhancing federal policy support.

The U.S. biofuels sector responded to these government incentives by expanding output every year from 1980 through 2011 (with the exception of 1996), with important implications for the domestic and international food and fuel sectors. Production of the primary U.S. biofuel, ethanol (derived from corn starch), has risen from about 175 million gallons in 1980 to nearly 14 billion gallons in 2011. U.S. biodiesel production (derived primarily from vegetable oil), albeit much smaller, has also shown strong growth, rising from

0.5 million gallons in 1999 to a record 969 million gallons in 2012. Despite the rapid growth of the past decades, total agriculture-based biofuels consumption accounted for only about 8% of U.S. transportation fuel consumption (9.7% of gasoline and 1.5% of diesel) in 2012.

Federal biofuels policies have had costs, including unintended market and environmental consequences and large federal outlays (estimated at $7.7 billion in 2011, but declining to $1.3 billion in 2012 with the expiration of the ethanol blender's tax credit). Despite the direct and indirect costs of federal biofuels policy and the relatively small role of biofuels as an energy source, the U.S. biofuels sector continues to push for federal involvement. But critics of federal policy intervention in the biofuels sector have also emerged. Current issues and policy developments related to the U.S. biofuels sector that are of interest to Congress include

- Many federal biofuels policies require routine congressional monitoring and occasional reconsideration in the form of reauthorization or new appropriations.
- The 10% ethanol-to-gasoline blend ratio—known as the "blend wall"—poses a barrier to expansion of ethanol use. The Environmental Protection Agency (EPA) issued waivers to allow ethanol blending of up to 15% (per gallon of gasoline) for use in model year 2001 and newer light-duty motor vehicles. However, the limitation to newer vehicles, coupled with infrastructure issues, could limit rapid expansion of blending rates.
- The slow development of cellulosic biofuels has raised concerns about the industry's ability to meet large federal usage mandates, which in turn has raised the potential for future EPA waivers of mandated biofuel volumes and has contributed to a cycle of slow investment in and development of the sector.

In 2012, the expiration of the blender tax credit, poor profit margins (due primarily to high corn prices), and the emerging blend wall limitation have contributed to a drop-off in ethanol production and have generated considerable uncertainty about the ethanol industry's future.

Chapter 4 – The Biomass Crop Assistance Program (BCAP) is designed to assist the bioenergy industry to overcome the hurdle of continuous biomass availability—viewed as a critical deterrent to private sector investment in the cellulosic biofuels industry. To accomplish this, BCAP is charged with two tasks: (1) to support the establishment and production of eligible crops for conversion to bioenergy in selected areas, and (2) to assist agricultural and forest land owners and operators with collection, harvest, storage, and transportation of eligible material for use in a biomass conversion facility.

BCAP was created in 2008 by the Food, Conservation, and Energy Act of 2008 (P.L. 110-246, 2008 farm bill). The 2014 farm bill (Agricultural Act of 2014; P.L. 113-79) extends BCAP through FY2018, with some modifications to its implementation.

BCAP is administered by the U.S. Department of Agriculture's (USDA's) Farm Service Agency (FSA). BCAP provides two categories of financial assistance: (1) annual and establishment payments that share in the cost of establishing and maintaining production of eligible biomass crops; and (2) matching payments that share in the cost of the collection, harvest, storage, and transportation of biomass to an eligible biomass conversion facility. The payments have different eligibility and sign-up requirements, payment rates, and contract lengths. BCAP assistance for establishing and producing biomass crops is available within designated project areas. BCAP project areas are specific geographic areas where producers may enroll land into BCAP contracts and produce specified biomass crops. As of June 2012, eleven BCAP project areas had been approved.

Under the 2008 farm bill, BCAP was authorized to receive such sums as necessary, meaning that funding for BCAP was both mandatory through the Commodity Credit Corporation and open-ended since it depended on program participation. However, Congress—as part of the annual appropriations process—capped BCAP funding in FY2010, FY2011, and FY2012. In response to funding reductions, USDA temporarily suspended the CHST matching payment portion of the program through FY2011, and re-prioritized future program funds in favor of uses that emphasize annual and establishment payments, especially under existing contracts, over CHST matching payments.

Under the 2014 farm bill, BCAP is authorized with mandatory funding of $25 million for each of FY2014 through FY2018; no discretionary funding is authorized.

In: The 2014 Farm Bill
Editor: Wilmer Combs

ISBN: 978-1-63321-432-3
© 2014 Nova Science Publishers, Inc.

Chapter 1

WHAT IS THE FARM BILL?*

Renée Johnson and Jim Monke

SUMMARY

The farm bill is an omnibus, multi-year piece of authorizing legislation that governs an array of agricultural and food programs. Titles in the most recent farm bill encompassed farm commodity price and income supports, farm credit, trade, agricultural conservation, research, rural development, bioenergy, foreign food aid, and domestic nutrition assistance. Although agricultural policies sometimes are created and changed by freestanding legislation or as part of other major laws, the farm bill provides a predictable opportunity for policy makers to comprehensively and periodically address agricultural and food issues. The farm bill is renewed about every five years.

The Agricultural Act of 2014 (P.L. 113-79) is the most recent omnibus farm bill, and was enacted into law in February 2014. It succeeded the Food, Conservation, and Energy Act of 2008 (P.L. 110-246). Provisions in the 2014 farm bill reshape the structure of farm commodity support, expand crop insurance coverage, consolidate conservation programs, reauthorize and revise nutrition assistance, and extend authority to appropriate funds for many U.S. Department of Agriculture (USDA) discretionary programs through FY2018.

---

* This is an edited, reformatted and augmented version of a Congressional Research Service publication RS22131, prepared for Members and Committees of Congress, dated April 7, 2014.

The Congressional Budget Office (CBO) estimates the total cost of mandatory programs at $489 billion over the next five years (FY2014-FY2018). This estimated cost does not include the cost of discretionary programs that are subject to appropriations. Of the total estimated mandatory outlays, $391 billion is for nutrition assistance and $98 billion is mostly geared toward agriculture production. Within the agriculture portion, crop insurance outlays are projected to be $41 billion over the next five years, $28 billion for conservation, and $24 billion for farm commodity programs. The trade title is projected to spend $1.8 billion over the next five years, horticulture $0.9 billion, research $0.8 billion, and bioenergy $0.6 billion. Accordingly, the overwhelming share (99%) of estimated total net mandatory outlays is anticipated for four farm bill titles: nutrition, crop insurance, conservation, and farm commodity support. Of the projected net outlays, about 80% is for the Supplemental Nutrition Assistance Program (SNAP, formerly known as food stamps). Farm commodity support and crop insurance are expected to account for 13% of mandatory program costs, with another 6% of costs in USDA conservation programs. Programs in all other farm bill titles are expected to account for about 1% of all mandatory expenditures.

WHAT IS THE FARM BILL?

The farm bill is an omnibus, multi-year piece of authorizing legislation that governs an array of agricultural and food programs. Although agricultural policies sometimes are created and changed by freestanding legislation or as part of other major laws, the farm bill provides a predictable opportunity for policy makers to comprehensively and periodically address agricultural and food issues. The farm bill is renewed about every five years.

Since the 1930s, farm bills traditionally have focused on farm commodity program support for a handful of staple commodities—corn, soybeans, wheat, cotton, rice, dairy, and sugar. Yet farm bills have grown in breadth in recent decades. Among the most prominent additions have been nutrition assistance, conservation, horticulture, and bioenergy programs.[1]

The omnibus nature of the farm bill can create broad coalitions of support among sometimes conflicting interests for policies that individually might not survive the legislative process. This can stir fierce competition for funds. In recent years, more parties have become involved in the debate, including national farm groups, commodity associations, state organizations, and nutrition and public health officials, as well as advocacy groups representing conservation, recreation, rural development, faith-based interests, local food systems, and certified organic production.

The Agricultural Act of 2014 (P.L. 113-79, H.Rept. 113-333), referred to here as the "2014 farm bill," is the most recent omnibus farm bill. It was enacted in February 2014 and succeeded the Food, Conservation, and Energy Act of 2008 (P.L. 110-246, "2008 farm bill"). The 2014 farm bill contains 12 titles encompassing commodity price and income supports, farm credit, trade, agricultural conservation, research, rural development, energy, and foreign and domestic food programs, among other programs.[2] (See titles described in the text box below.)

Provisions in the 2014 farm bill reshape the structure of farm commodity support, expand crop insurance coverage, consolidate conservation programs, reauthorize and revise nutrition assistance, and extend authority to appropriate funds for many U.S. Department of Agriculture (USDA) discretionary programs through FY2018. USDA reports that implementing the 2014 farm bill will require about 150 rulemaking actions, and more than 40 studies and reports.

As the 2008 farm bill was approaching expiration, Congress considered an omnibus farm bill to reauthorize expiring programs and to establish the direction of agriculture and food policy for the next several years. Many 2008 farm bill provisions expired in September 2012 but were extended for an additional year, though some had no funding.[3] The 112th Congress began work on a farm bill but did not complete it, requiring new bills to be introduced in the 113th Congress.

When a farm bill expires, not all programs are affected equally. The authority for most programs expires—some cease to operate altogether unless reauthorized, while others might continue to pay old obligations. Nutrition assistance programs require periodic reauthorization, but appropriations can keep them operating. The farm commodity programs not only expire, but would revert to permanent law dating back to the 1940s. Many discretionary programs would lose statutory authority to receive appropriations, though annual appropriations could provide funding. Other programs have permanent authority and do not need to be reauthorized (e.g., crop insurance).[4]

Figure 1 provides a timeline of selected important dates for U.S. farm bill policy and other related laws. In many respects, agricultural policy in the United States began with the creation of USDA, homesteading, and subsequent creation of the land grant universities in the 1800s. Many stand-alone agricultural laws were passed through the early 1900s to address help farmers with credit availability and marketing practices, and to protect consumers via meat inspection.

The 2014 Farm Bill (P.L. 113-79): Functions and Major Issues, by Title

- *Title I, Commodity Programs:* Provides farm payments when crop prices or revenues decline for major commodity crops, including wheat, corn, soybeans, peanuts, and rice. Includes disaster programs to help livestock and tree fruit producers manage production losses due to natural disasters. Other support includes margin insurance for dairy and marketing quotas, minimum price guarantees, and import barriers for sugar.
- *Title II, Conservation:* Encourages environmental stewardship and improved management practices. Working lands programs include Environmental Quality Incentives Program (EQIP) and Conservation Stewardship Program (CSP). Land retirement programs include the Conservation Reserve Program (CRP). Other aid is in the Agricultural Conservation Easement Program (ACEP) and Regional Conservation Partnership Program (RCPP).
- *Title III, Trade:* Provides support for U.S. agricultural export programs and international food assistance programs. Major programs included Market Access Program (MAP) and the primary U.S. food aid program, Food for Peace, which provides emergency and nonemergency food aid, among other programs. Other provisions address program changes related to World Trade Organization (WTO) obligations.
- *Title IV, Nutrition:* Provides nutrition assistance for low-income households through programs including the Supplemental Nutrition Assistance Program (SNAP, formerly known as food stamps) and The Emergency Food Assistance Program (TEFAP). Also supports the distribution of foods in schools.
- *Title V, Credit:* Provides support for federal direct and guaranteed loans to farmers and ranchers, and loan eligibility rules and policies.
- *Title VI, Rural Development:* Supports business and community programs for planning, feasibility assessments, and coordination with other local, state, and federal programs. Programs include grants and loans for infrastructure, economic development, broadband and telecommunications, among other programs.
- *Title VII, Research, Extension, and Related Matters:* Supports a wide range of agricultural research and extension programs that help farmers and ranchers become more efficient, innovative, and productive.

Other types of research programs include biosecurity and response, biotechnology, and organic production.

- *Title VIII, Forestry:* Supports forestry management programs run by USDA's Forest Service.
- *Title IX, Energy:* Supports the development of farm and community renewable energy systems through grants, loan guarantees, and procurement assistance initiatives. Provisions cover the production, marketing, and processing of biofuels and biofuel feedstocks, and research, education, and demonstration programs.
- *Title X, Horticulture:* Supports specialty crops—fruits, vegetables, tree nuts, and floriculture and ornamental products—through a range of initiatives, including market promotion; plant pest and disease prevention; and public research; among other initiatives. Also provides assistance to support certified organic agricultural production.
- *Title XI, Crop Insurance:* Enhances the permanently authorized federal crop insurance program. New plans include Stacked Income Protection (STAX) for cotton and Supplemental Coverage Option (SCO) for other crops.
- *Title XII, Miscellaneous:* Programs not covered in other titles, including provisions affecting livestock and poultry production and limited-resource and socially disadvantaged farmers, among other provisions.

The economic depression and dust bowl in the 1930s prompted the first "farm bill" in 1933, with subsidies and production controls to raise farm incomes and simultaneously encourage conservation practices. Commodity subsidies continued to evolve though the 1960s farm bills. The Great Society reforms then drew attention to food assistance. The 1973 farm bill was the first "omnibus" farm bill, since it not only included farm supports but also food stamp reauthorization. Subsequent farm bills continued to expand in scope, adding titles that addressed formerly standalone laws such as trade, credit, and crop insurance. New conservation laws were part of the 1985 farm bill, organic agriculture in the 1990 farm bill, research programs in the 1996 farm bill, bioenergy in the 2002 farm bill, and horticulture and local food systems in the 2008 farm bill.

WHAT IS THE COST?

The farm bill authorizes programs in two spending categories: mandatory and discretionary. Mandatory programs generally operate as entitlements; the farm bill pays for them using multiyear budget estimates when the law is enacted. Discretionary programs are authorized for their scope, but are not funded in the farm bill; they are subject to appropriations. While both types of programs are important, mandatory programs often dominate the farm bill debate.

Farm Bill at Enactment

At enactment of the 2014 farm bill, the Congressional Budget Office (CBO) estimated the total cost of mandatory programs would be $489 billion over the next five years (FY2014-FY2018).[5] The overwhelming share (99%) of estimated total net outlays is anticipated for four farm bill titles (*Figure 2*). About 80% is for the Supplemental Nutrition Assistance Program (SNAP). Farm commodity support and crop insurance are expected to account for 13% of mandatory program costs, with another 6% of costs in USDA conservation programs.

Table 1. 2014 Farm Bill Budget: Baseline, Scores, and Projected Outlays, by Title (mandatory outlays in millions of dollars, five-year total FY2014-FY2018)

2014 Farm Bill Titles		CBO baseline FY2014-FY2018	CBO Score (change to baseline) of P.L. 113-79	Projected Outlays (Baseline + Score) of P.L. 113-79	Share
I	Commodities	29,888	-6,332	23,556	4.8%
II	Conservation	28,373	-208	28,165	5.8%
III	Trade	1,718	+64	1,782	0.4%
IV	Nutrition	393,930	-3,280	390,650	79.9%
V	Credit	-1,011	+0	-1,011	-0.2%
VI	Rural Dev.	13	+205	218	0.04%
VII	Research	111	+689	800	0.2%
VIII	Forestry	3	+5	8	0.002%
IX	Energy	84	+541	625	0.1%
X	Horticulture	536	+338	874	0.2%
XI	Crop Ins.	39,592	+1,828	41,420	8.5%
XII	Misc. (NAP)	705	+839	1,544	0.3%
Total, Direct Spending		493,941	-5,310[a]	488,631[a]	100.0%

Source: CRS, using the CBO baseline and 2014 farm bill cost estimates (http://www.cbo.gov/ publication/45049).

[a] Including changes in revenues, the 5-year net impact on the deficit is an estimated change of -$5.361 billion.

On a 10-year basis, the score is -$16.608 billion, with 10-year projected outlays of $956.4 billion.

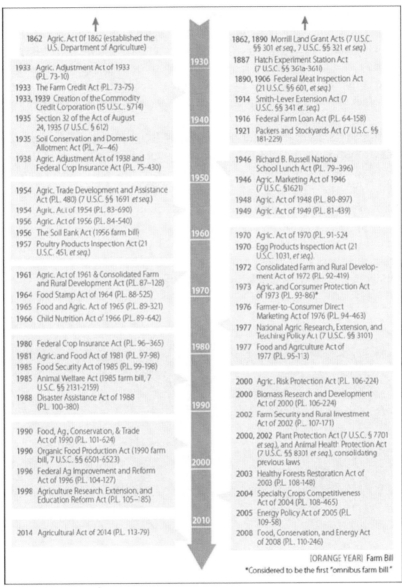

Source: CRS.

Figure 1. Important Dates for U.S. Farm Bill Policy and Selected Related Laws.

Programs in all other farm bill titles are expected to account for about 1% of all mandatory expenditures.

Of the total estimated mandatory outlays, $391 billion is for nutrition assistance and $98 billion is mostly geared toward agriculture production.[6] Within the agriculture portion, crop insurance outlays are projected to be $41 billion over the next five years, $28 billion for conservation, and $24 billion for farm commodity programs. The trade title is projected to spend $1.8 billion over the next five years, horticulture $0.9 billion, research $0.8 billion, and bioenergy $0.6 billion.[7]

If the 2008 farm bill had continued, CBO estimated that mandatory outlays would have been $494 billion for the five-year period FY2014-FY2018.[8] Compared to this baseline, the 2014 farm bill reduces projected spending and the deficit by $5.3 billion (-1.1%) over five years. The net reduction is composed of some titles receiving more funding, while other titles provide offsets. The titles for farm commodity subsidies, nutrition, and conservation provide budgetary savings. The titles for crop insurance, research, bioenergy, horticulture, rural development, trade, forestry, and miscellaneous items receive additional funding (*Table 1*).

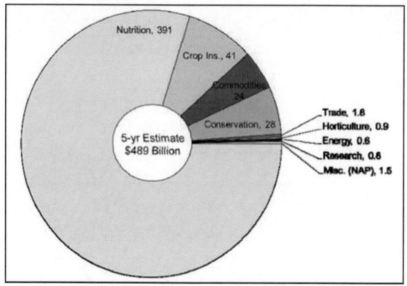

Source: CRS, using CBO's 2014 farm bill cost estimates (http://www.cbo.gov/publication/45049).

Figure 2. Projected Outlays in the 2014 Farm Bill. (five-year projected mandatory outlays FY2014-FY2018 in billions of dollars by title).

TITLE-BY-TITLE SUMMARIES

Following are summaries of the major provisions of each title of the 2014 farm bill.

Title I: Commodity Programs[9]

Under the enacted 2014 farm bill, farm support for traditional commodity crops—grains, oilseeds, and cotton—is restructured by eliminating direct payments,[10] the counter-cyclical price (CCP) program, and the Average Crop Revenue Election (ACRE) program.[11] Under the 2014 farm bill, producers may choose between the following two programs linked to a decline in either price or revenue (price times crop yield): (1) Price Loss Coverage or PLC, which retains a counter-cyclical price program and makes a farm payment when farm price for a covered crop declines below its "reference price" set in statute; and (2) Agriculture Risk Coverage (ARC), which retains a revenue-based program, is designed to cover a portion of a farmer's out-of-pocket loss (referred to as "shallow loss") when crop revenues decline. These farm programs are separate from a producer's decision to purchase crop insurance. The 2014 farm bill makes significant changes to U.S. dairy policy by eliminating the dairy product price support program, the Milk Income Loss Contract (MILC) program, and export subsidies. These are replaced by a new program, which makes payments to participating dairy producers when the national margin (average farm price of milk minus an average feed cost ration) falls below a producer-selected margin. The farm bill does not change the objective and structure of the U.S. sugar program. The 2014 farm bill also sets a $125,000 per person cap on the total of PLC, ARC, marketing loan gains, and loan deficiency payments. It also makes changes to the eligibility requirement based on adjusted gross income (AGI), setting a new limit to a single, total AGI limit of $900,000.

The bill retroactively reauthorizes and funds four programs covering livestock and tree assistance, beginning in FY2012 and continuing without an expiration date. The crop disaster program from the 2008 farm bill (i.e., Supplemental Revenue Assistance, or SURE) was not reauthorized, but elements of it are folded into the new ARC program by allowing producers to protect against farm-level revenue losses. Provisions in other farm bill titles provide disaster benefits to tree fruit producers who suffered crop losses in

2012, and additional coverage levels are authorized under the Noninsured Crop Assistance Program (NAP).

Title II: Conservation[12]

Prior to the 2014 farm bill, the agricultural conservation portfolio included over 20 conservation programs. The bill reduces and consolidates the number of conservation programs, and reduces mandatory funding. It reauthorizes many of the larger existing conservation programs, such as the Conservation Reserve Program (CRP), the Environmental Quality Incentives Program (EQIP), and the Conservation Stewardship Program (CSP), and rolled smaller and similar conservation programs into two new conservation programs—the Agricultural Conservation Easement Program (ACEP) and the Regional Conservation Partnership Program (RCPP). Previous conservation easement programs, including programs related to wetlands, grasslands, and farmland protection, were repealed and consolidated to create ACEP. ACEP retains most of the program provisions in the previous easement programs by establishing two types of easements: wetland reserve easements that protect and restore wetlands, and agricultural land easements that prevent non-agricultural uses on productive farm or grasslands. Previous programs focused on agricultural water enhancement, and two programs related to the Chesapeake Bay and Great Lakes, among other programs, were repealed and consolidated into the new RCPP. RCPP will use partnership agreements with state and local governments, Indian tribes, farmer cooperatives, and other conservation organizations to leverage federal funding and further conservation on a regional or watershed scale.

The 2014 farm bill also adds the federally funded portion of crop insurance premiums to the list of program benefits that could be lost if a producer is found to produce an agricultural commodity on highly erodible land without implementing an approved conservation plan or qualifying exemption, or converts a wetland to crop production. This prerequisite, referred to as conservation compliance, has existed since the 1985 farm bill and previously affected most USDA farm program benefits, but has excluded crop insurance since 1996.

Title III: Trade[13]

The 2014 farm bill reauthorizes and amends USDA's food aid, export market development, and export credit guarantee programs. The bill reauthorizes all of the international food aid programs, including the largest, Food for Peace Title II[14] (emergency and nonemergency food aid), and also amends existing food aid law to place greater emphasis on improving the nutritional quality of food aid products and ensuring that sales of agricultural commodity donations do not disrupt local markets, among other changes. The bill creates a new local and regional purchase program in place of the expired local and regional procurement (LRP) pilot program of the 2008 farm bill and increases the authorized appropriations for the program. The 2014 farm bill also reauthorizes funding for the Commodity Credit Corporation (CCC) Export Credit Guarantee program and three other agricultural export market promotion programs, including the Market Access Program (MAP), which finances promotional activities for both generic and branded U.S. agricultural products, and the Foreign Market Development Program (FMDP), a generic commodity promotion program. It also made changes to the credit guarantee program to comply with the WTO cotton case against the United States won by Brazil, and proposes a plan to reorganize the trade functions of USDA, including establishing an agency position to coordinate sanitary and phytosanitary matters and address agricultural non-tariff trade barriers across agencies.

Title IV: Nutrition[15]

The 2014 farm bill's nutrition title accounts for 80% of the law's forecasted spending. The majority of the law's Nutrition funding and policies pertain to the Supplemental Nutrition Assistance Program (SNAP), which provides benefits redeemable for eligible foods at eligible retailers to eligible, low-income individuals. The bill reauthorizes SNAP and The Emergency Food Assistance Program (TEFAP, the program that provides USDA foods and federal support to emergency feeding organizations such as food banks and food pantries), and other related programs, and is estimated by CBO to reduce related spending.[16] The bill retains most of the eligibility and benefit calculation rules in SNAP. It does, however, amend how Low-Income Home Energy Assistance Program (LIHEAP) payments are treated in the calculation of SNAP benefits.[17] It includes certain other eligibility disqualifications, including the disqualification of certain ex-offenders from receiving SNAP benefits if they do not comply with the terms of their sentence. The law establishes a number of new policies related to the SNAP Employment and Training (E&T) program, including a pilot project authority and related funding for states to implement and USDA to evaluate work programs for SNAP participants.[18] The bill makes changes to SNAP law pertaining to retailer authorization and benefit issuance and redemption, including requiring stores to stock a greater variety of foods and more fresh foods, requiring retailers to pay for their electronic benefit transfer (EBT) machines, and providing additional funding for combatting trafficking (the sale of SNAP benefits). It also includes new federal funding to support organizations that offer bonus incentives for SNAP purchases of fruits and vegetables (called Food Insecurity Nutrition Incentive grants). The bill also increases funding for TEFAP. It also includes other changes to SNAP and related programs, including amendments to the nutrition programs operated by tribes and territories, the Commodity Supplemental Food Program (CSFP), and the distribution of USDA foods to schools.[19]

Title V: Credit[20]

The 2014 farm bill makes relatively minor changes to the permanent statutes for two types of farm lenders: the USDA Farm Service Agency (FSA) and the Farm Credit System (FCS).[21] It gives USDA discretion to recognize alternative legal entities to qualify for farm loans and allow alternatives to meet a three-year farming experience requirement. It increases the maximum size of down-payment loans, and eliminates term limits on guaranteed operating loans (by removing a maximum number of years that an individual can remain eligible). It increases the percentage of a conservation loan that can be guaranteed, adds another lending priority for beginning farmers, and facilitates loans for the purchase of highly fractionated land in Indian reservations, among other changes.

Title VI: Rural Development[22]

The 2014 farm bill reauthorizes and/or amends rural development loan and grant programs and authorized several new provisions, including rural infrastructure, economic development, and broadband and telecommunications development, among other programs. The bill reauthorizes funding for programs under the Rural Electrification Act of 1936, including the Access to Broadband Telecommunications Services in Rural Areas Program and the Distance Learning and Telemedicine Program, and also reauthorizes the Northern Great Plains Regional Authority and the three regional authorities established in the 2008 farm bill. It also increases funding for several programs, including the Value-Added Agricultural Product Grants, rural development loans and grants, and the Microentrepreneur Assistance Program. The bill retains the definition of "rural" and "rural area" under current law for purposes of program eligibility; however, it amends the definition of rural area in the 1949 Housing Act so that areas deemed rural between 2000 and 2010 would retain that designation until USDA receives data from the 2020 decennial census. The provision further raises the population threshold for eligibility from 25,000 to 35,000. The bill also authorizes USDA to prioritize otherwise eligible applications that support multijurisdictional strategic economic and community development, as well as a new Rural Energy Savings Program, and amends the water and waste water direct and guaranteed loan programs, among other changes to USDA's rural development programs.

Title VII: Research[23]

USDA is authorized under various laws to conduct agricultural research at the federal level, and to provide support for cooperative research, extension, and post-secondary agricultural education programs in the states. The 2014 farm bill reauthorizes funding for these activities through FY2018, subject to annual appropriations, and amends authority so that only competitive grants can be awarded under certain programs. Mandatory spending for the research title is increased for several programs, including the Specialty Crop Research Initiative and the Organic Agricultural Research and Extension Initiative. Also, mandatory funding is continued for the Beginning Farmer and Rancher Development Program. The bill provides mandatory funding to establish the Foundation for Food and Agriculture Research, a nonprofit corporation designed to supplement USDA's basic and applied research activities to solicit and accept private donations to award grants for collaborative public/private partnerships with scientists at USDA and in academia, nonprofits, and the private sector.

Title VIII: Forestry[24]

General forestry legislation is within the jurisdiction of the Agriculture Committees, and past farm bills have included provisions addressing forestry assistance, especially on private lands. The 2014 farm bill generally repeals, reauthorizes, and modifies existing programs and provisions under two main authorities: the Cooperative Forestry Assistance Act (CFAA), as amended, and the Healthy Forests Restoration Act of 2003 (HFRA), as amended. Many federal forestry assistance programs are permanently authorized, and thus do not require reauthorization in the farm bill. However, the 2014 farm bill reauthorizes several other forestry assistance programs through FY2018. It also repeals programs that have expired or have never received appropriations. The bill also includes provisions that address the management of the National Forest System, and also authorizes the designation of treatment areas within the National Forest System that are of deteriorating forest health due to insect or disease infestation, and allows for expedited project planning within those designated areas.

Title IX: Energy[25]

USDA renewable energy programs have been used to incentivize research, development, and adoption of renewable energy projects, including solar, wind, and anaerobic digesters. However, the primary focus of these programs has been to promote U.S. biofuels production and use. Cornstarch-based ethanol dominates the U.S. biofuels industry. Earlier, the 2008 farm bill refocused U.S. biofuels policy initiatives in favor of non-corn feedstocks, especially the development of the cellulosic biofuels industry. The most critical programs to this end are the Bioenergy Program for Advanced Biofuels (pays producers for production of eligible advanced biofuels); the Biorefinery Assistance Program (assists in the development of new and emerging technologies for advanced biofuels); the Biomass Crop Assistance Program, BCAP (assists farmers in developing nontraditional crops for use as feedstocks for the eventual production of cellulosic biofuels); and the Renewable Energy for America Program, REAP (funds a variety of biofuels-related projects). The 2014 farm bill extends most of the renewable energy provisions of the 2008 farm bill through FY2018 with some notable modifications to REAP and BCAP, repeals four provisions, and adds a new reporting requirement.

Title X: Horticulture and Organic Agriculture[26]

The 2014 farm bill reauthorizes many of the existing farm bill provisions supporting farming operations in the specialty crop and certified organic sectors. Many provisions fall into the categories of marketing and promotion; organic certification; data and information collection; pest and disease control; food safety and quality standards; and local foods. The bill adopts nearly all the programs, and in some cases provides for increased funding for several key programs benefitting specialty crop producers. These include the Specialty Crop Block Grant Program, plant pest and disease programs, USDA's Market News for specialty crops, the Specialty Crop Research Initiative (SCRI), and the Fresh Fruit and Vegetable Program (Snack Program) and Section 32 purchases for fruits and vegetables under the Nutrition title. The final law also reauthorizes most programs benefitting certified organic agriculture producers provisions as well as provisions that expand opportunities for local food systems and also beginning farmers and ranchers.[27] Provisions affecting the specialty crop and certified organic sectors are not limited to this title, but are contained within several other titles of the farm bill. These include programs in the research, nutrition, and trade titles, among others.

Title XI: Crop Insurance[28]

The crop insurance title enhances the existing federal crop insurance program, which is permanently authorized by the Federal Crop Insurance Act. The federal crop insurance program makes available subsidized crop insurance to producers who purchase a policy to protect against losses in yield, crop revenue, or whole farm revenue. More than 100 crops are insurable. The 2014 farm bill increases funding for crop insurance relative to baseline levels, most of which is for two new insurance products, one for cotton and one for other crops. With cotton not covered by the counter-cyclical price or revenue programs established in Title I, a new crop insurance policy called Stacked Income Protection Plan (STAX) is made available for cotton producers. For other crops, the 2014 farm bill makes available an additional policy called Supplemental Coverage Option (SCO), based on expected county yields or revenue, to cover part of the deductible under the producer's underlying policy (referred to as a farmer's out-of-pocket loss or "shallow loss"). Additional crop insurance changes in the 2014 farm bill are designed to expand or improve crop insurance for other commodities, including specialty crops.

Provisions revise the value of crop insurance for organic crops to reflect prices of organic (not conventional) crops. USDA is required to conduct more research on whole farm revenue insurance with higher coverage levels than currently available.

Title XII: Miscellaneous

The miscellaneous title in the 2014 farm bill includes various provisions affecting livestock production;[29] socially disadvantaged and limited-resource producers; and oilheat efficiency, research, and jobs training, among other provisions. The livestock provisions include animal health-related and also animal welfare provisions, creation of a production and marketing grant program for the sheep industry, and requirements that USDA finalize the rules on catfish inspection and also conduct a study of its country-of-origin labeling (COOL) rule. The farm bill also extends authority for outreach and technical assistance programs for socially disadvantaged farmers and ranchers and adds military veteran farmers and ranchers as a qualifying group. It also creates a research center to develop policy recommendations for socially disadvantaged farmers and ranchers, reauthorizes funding for the USDA Office of Advocacy and Outreach for socially disadvantaged and veteran farmers and ranchers, and includes a provision to increase transparency by automatically providing receipts for service or denial of service. It also creates a military veterans agricultural liaison within USDA to advocate for and to provide information to veterans, and establishes an Office of Tribal Relations to coordinate USDA activities with Native American tribes. Other provisions establish grants for maple syrup producers and trust funds for cotton and wool apparel manufacturers and citrus growers, and also provide technological training for farm workers, as well as provisions related to the Environmental Protection Agency.

End Notes

[1] There have been 17 farm bills since the 1930s (2014, 2008, 2002, 1996, 1990, 1985, 1981, 1977, 1973, 1970, 1965, 1956, 1954, 1949, 1948, 1938, and 1933). Farm bills have become increasingly omnibus in nature since 1973, with the inclusion of a nutrition title.

[2] For more information, see CRS Report R43076, The 2014 Farm Bill (P.L. 113-79): Summary and Side-by-Side.

[3] For more information, see CRS Report R41433, Expiring Farm Bill Programs Without a Budget Baseline.

[4] For more information, see CRS Report R42442, Expiration and Extension of the 2008 Farm Bill.

[5] CBO cost estimate of the Agricultural Act of 2014, January 28, 2014 (http://www.cbo.gov/publication/45049).

[6] The 10-year projected total cost is $956 billion, with $756 billion for nutrition and $200 billion for agriculture.

[7] More details on the farm bill budget are available in CRS Report R42484, Budget Issues Shaping a Farm Bill in 2013.

[8] CBO, "May 2013 Baseline for the 2008 Farm Bill Programs and Provisions, by Title," unpublished, May 2013. See also "Updated Budget Projections: Fiscal Years 2013 to 2023," May 14, 2013, at http://cbo.gov/ publication/44172.

[9] For more direct assistance regarding commodity crops, contact Dennis Shields (dshields@crs.loc.gov, 7-9051); for dairy, contact Randy Schnepf (rschnepf@crs.loc,gov, 7-4277); for sugar, contact Remy Jurenas (rjurenas@crs.loc.gov, 7-7281); and for payment limits, contact Jim Monke (jmonke@crs.loc.gov, 7-9664).

[10] Since 1996, direct payments have been made to producers and landowners based on historical production of corn, wheat, soybeans, cotton, rice, peanuts, and other "covered" crops. Cotton producers will receive direct payment assistance in crop years 2014 and 2015 as they transition to the STAX insurance product (see Title XI, Crop Insurance).

[11] For information, see CRS Report R42759, Farm Safety Net Provisions in a 2013 Farm Bill: S. 954 and H.R. 2642.

[12] For more direct assistance, contact Megan Stubbs (mstubbs@crs.loc.gov, 7-8707). For more information, see CRS Report R40763, Agricultural Conservation: A Guide to Programs.

[13] For more direct assistance regarding international food aid, contact Randy Schnepf (rschnepf@crs.loc,gov, 7-4277); for agricultural export programs, contact Remy Jurenas (rjurenas@crs.loc.gov, 7-7281).

[14] Alternatively referred to as Food for Peace (P.L. 480) Title II.

[15] For more direct assistance, contact Randy Alison Aussenberg (raussenberg@crs.loc.gov, 7-8641). For more information, see CRS Report R42505, Supplemental Nutrition Assistance Program (SNAP): A Primer on Eligibility and Benefits; and CRS Report R42353, Domestic Food Assistance: Summary of Programs.

[16] The SNAP provisions alone are estimated to reduce spending by $8.6 billion over 10 years, while certain other title provisions are estimated to increase spending, which together result in the total estimated reduction of $8.0 billion.

[17] CRS Report R42591, The 2014 Farm Bill: Changing the Treatment of LIHEAP Receipt in the Calculation of SNAP Benefits.

[18] The bill does not include changes to broad-based categorical eligibility or a state option to drug test SNAP applicants; these options has been included in House proposals.

[19] The 2010 child nutrition reauthorization (Healthy, Hunger-Free Kids Act of 2010, P.L. 111-296) had already reauthorized some nutrition programs through FY2015, but P.L. 113-79 included certain related policy changes. See CRS Report R41354, Child Nutrition and WIC Reauthorization: P.L. 111-296.

[20] For more direct assistance, contact Jim Monke (jmonke@crs.loc.gov, 7-9664). For more information, see CRS Report RS21977, Agricultural Credit: Institutions and Issues.

[21] The Consolidated Farm and Rural Development Act is the permanent statute that authorizes USDA agricultural credit and rural development programs. The Farm Credit Act of 1971, as

amended, is the permanent statute that authorizes the Farm Credit System. See CRS Report RS21977, Agricultural Credit: Institutions and Issues.

[22] For more direct assistance, contact Tadlock Cowan (tcowan@crs.loc.gov, 7-7660). For more information, see CRS Report RL31837, An Overview of USDA Rural Development Programs.

[23] For more direct assistance, contact Dennis Shields (dshields@crs.loc.gov, 7-9051). For more information, see CRS Report R40819, USDA's Research, Education, and Economics (REE) Mission Area: Issues and Background.

[24] For more direct assistance, contact Katie Hoover (lhoover@crs.loc.gov, 7-9008). For more information, see CRS Report RL31065, Forestry Assistance Programs

[25] For more direct assistance, contact Randy Schnepf (rschnepf@crs.loc,gov, 7-4277). For more information, see CRS Report R43416, Energy Provisions in the 2014 Farm Bill (P.L. 113-79).

[26] For more direct assistance, contact Renée Johnson (rjohnson@crs.loc.gov, 7-9588). For more information, see CRS Report R42771, Fruits, Vegetables, and Other Specialty Crops: Selected Federal Programs.

[27] Other provisions supporting local food producers are within the research, nutrition, and rural development titles, among other titles.

[28] For more direct assistance, contact Dennis Shields (dshields@crs.loc.gov, 7-9051). For more information, see CRS Report RS21212, Agricultural Disaster Assistance and CRS Report R40532, Federal Crop Insurance: Background.

[29] The 2008 farm bill included new livestock-related provisions under a new bill title, and made changes to existing laws governing livestock and poultry marketing and competition. A separate livestock title was not included in the 2014 farm bill. For more direct assistance, contact Joel L. Greene (jgreene@crs.loc.gov, 7-9877). For more information, see CRS Report R42954, Animal Agriculture: Selected Issues in the 113th Congress.

In: The 2014 Farm Bill
Editor: Wilmer Combs

ISBN: 978-1-63321-432-3
© 2014 Nova Science Publishers, Inc.

Chapter 2

ENERGY PROVISIONS IN THE 2014 FARM BILL (P.L. 113-79)[*]

Randy Schnepf

SUMMARY

Title IX, the Energy title of the 2014 farm bill (Agricultural Act of 2014; P.L. 113-79), contains authority for the bioenergy programs administered by the U.S. Department of Agriculture (USDA). USDA renewable energy programs have incentivized research, development, and adoption of renewable energy projects, including solar, wind, and anaerobic digesters. However, the primary focus of USDA renewable energy programs has been to promote U.S. biofuels production and use— including corn starch-based ethanol, cellulosic ethanol, and soybean-based biodiesel.

Corn starch-based ethanol dominates the U.S. biofuels industry. The previous 2008 farm bill (P.L. 110-246) had attempted to refocus U.S. biofuels policy initiatives in favor of non-corn feedstocks, especially the development of the cellulosic biofuels industry. The most critical programs to this end are the Bioenergy Program for Advanced Biofuels, which pays producers for production of eligible advanced biofuels; the Biorefinery Assistance Program, which assists in the development of new and emerging technologies for advanced biofuels; the Biomass Crop Assistance Program (BCAP), which assists farmers in developing

---

[*] This is an edited, reformatted and augmented version of a Congressional Research Service publication, No. R43416, dated March 12, 2014.

nontraditional crops for use as feedstocks for the eventual production of cellulosic biofuels; and the Renewable Energy for America Program (REAP), which has funded a variety of biofuels-related projects, including the installation of blender pumps to help circumvent the emerging "blend wall" that has effectively circumscribed domestic ethanol consumption near current levels of about 13 billion gallons annually.

All of the major farm bill energy programs expired at the end of FY2013 and lacked baseline funding going forward. The enacted 2014 farm bill extends most of the renewable energy provisions of the 2008 farm bill with new funding authority, with the exception of the Rural Energy Self-Sufficiency Initiative, the Forest Biomass for Energy Program, the Biofuels Infrastructure Study, and the Renewable Fertilizer Study, which are either omitted or repealed. In addition, P.L. 113-79 includes a new provision which precludes the use of REAP funding for any mechanism for dispensing energy at the retail level (e.g., blender pumps). Also, despite several amendments to the contrary, and its explicit exclusion from all financial support in the House-passed version of the farm bill (H.R. 2642), BCAP funding for the Collection, Harvest, Storage, and Transportation (CHST) component is retained in P.L. 113-79. Elimination of CHST support would likely have severely limited BCAP's potential effectiveness as an incentive to produce cellulosic feedstocks. Finally, P.L. 113-79 adds a new reporting requirement on energy use and efficiency at USDA facilities.

Over the five-year reauthorization period (FY2014-FY2018), the 2014 farm bill contains a total of $694 million in new mandatory funding and authorizes discretionary funding (i.e., subject to annual appropriations) of $765 million for the various farm bill renewable energy programs. This contrasts with the previous 2008 farm bill, which had authorized slightly over $1 billion in mandatory funding for a five-year period (FY2008-FY2012) and $1.7 billion in discretionary appropriations to Title IX energy programs.

OVERVIEW

Agriculture-based renewable energy can take several forms, including biofuels such as corn-based ethanol or soy-based biodiesel, wind-driven turbines located on farmland or in rural areas, anaerobic digesters that convert animal waste into methane and electric power, or biomass harvested for burning as a processing fuel or to generate heat as part of an industrial activity.

Since the late 1970s, U.S. policy makers at both the federal and state levels have adopted a variety of incentives, regulations, and programs to encourage the production and use of agriculture-based renewable energy (mostly biofuels).[1] In particular, the two most widely used biofuels—ethanol produced primarily from corn starch and biodiesel produced primarily from soybean oil—have received significant federal support in the form of tax incentives, loans and grants, and regulatory programs.[2] Many of these support programs originate in legislation outside of the farm bill. Motivations cited for these legislative initiatives included energy security concerns, reduction of greenhouse gas emissions from traditional fossil fuels, and raising domestic demand for U.S.-produced farm products.

By FY2007 total direct federal biofuels subsidies had grown to over $4 billion per year.[3] By FY2011, federal biofuels subsidies had reached approximately $7.7 billion, of which an estimated $5.7 billion was attributable to the Volumetric Ethanol Excise Tax Credit (VEETC) of $0.45/gallon. However, the VEETC expired at the end of FY2011 and federal subsidies fell to an estimated $1.3 billion in FY2012—consisting primarily of biodiesel producer tax credits of approximately $1 billion. The remaining biofuels tax credits—for biodiesel and cellulosic biofuel, and including a small producers tax credit—expired at the end of FY2013. In their absence, the funding afforded under the provisions of Title IX of the 2014 farm bill represents the principal source of federal support for biofuels production and use in the United States.

This report focuses on those policies contained in the 2014 farm bill that support agriculture-based renewable energy, especially biofuels. The introductory sections of this report briefly describe how USDA bioenergy policies evolved and how they fit into the larger context of U.S. biofuels policy. Then, each of the bioenergy provisions of the 2014 farm bill are defined in terms of their function, goals, administration, funding, and implementation status.

In an appendix at the end of this report, Table A-5 presents data on 2014 farm bill budgetary authority for energy provisions, while Table A-6 presents the original budget authority for Title IX programs under the previous 2008 farm bill. A third table (Table A-7) provides a side-by-side comparison of Title IX energy-related provisions for current versus previous law.

Origins of Federal Biofuels Policy

Renewable energy production plays a key role not just in agricultural policy, but also in energy, tax, and environmental policy. As a result, many of the federal programs that support renewable energy production in general, and agriculture-based energy production in particular, are outside the purview of USDA and have origins outside of omnibus farm bill legislation. For example, the three principal federal biofuels policies of the past decade were all established outside of farm bills as follows.

- The Renewable Fuel Standard (RFS) mandates an increasing volume of biofuels use and has its origins in the Energy Policy Act of 2005 (P.L. 109-58). The RFS was expanded in the Energy Independence and Security Act of 2007 (EISA; P.L. 110-140) and divided into four distinct, but nested categories—biodiesel, cellulosic, advanced, and total—each with its own mandated volume.[4]
- The volumetric ethanol excise tax credit (VEETC), originally established in the American Jobs Creation Act of 2004 (P.L. 108-357), provided a tax credit that varied in value over the years, but was last at $0.45 per gallon of pure ethanol blended with gasoline when it expired on December 31, 2011.[5]
- The ethanol import tariff (a most-favored-nation duty of $0.54 per gallon) was intended to offset the blending tax credit and was originally established by the Omnibus Reconciliation Act of 1980 (P.L. 96-499). The ethanol import tariff also expired on December 31, 2011.[6]

In addition to the RFS, VEETC, and import tariff, several other tax credits that originated outside of farm bills were available for biodiesel production as well as for small producers (less than 60 million gallons per year per plant) of ethanol and biodiesel.[7] A substantial number of federal programs also support renewable energy sources other than biofuels.[8] In addition to federal programs, many states offer additional support to biofuels producers, blenders, and consumers.[9]

An awareness of the non-USDA federal programs is important for appreciating the role envisioned for the energy title of the 2014 farm bill, which is designed to provide incentives for the research and development of new agriculture-based renewable fuels, especially second-generation biofuels (based on non-food crop biomass such as cellulose and algae), and to expand their distribution and use.

2002 Farm Bill—First Energy Title

The 2002 farm bill (Farm Security and Rural Investment Act of 2002, P.L. 107-171) was the first omnibus farm bill to explicitly include an energy title (Title IX). The energy title authorized grants, loans, and loan guarantees to foster research on agriculture-based renewable energy, to share development risk and to promote the adoption of renewable energy systems.[10] Since enactment of the 2002 farm bill, interest in renewable energy has grown rapidly, due in large part to a strong rise in domestic and international petroleum prices and a dramatic acceleration in domestic biofuels production (primarily corn-based ethanol).

2008 Farm Bill—Refocus on Non-Corn-Based Biofuels

Annual U.S. ethanol production expanded rapidly between 2001 and 2011, rising from under 2 billion gallons to nearly 14 billion gallons during that period.[11] Similarly, corn use for ethanol grew from a 7% share of the U.S. corn crop in 2001, to an estimated 40% share of the 2011 corn crop.[12] In 2007 (during the 2008 farm bill debate), about 23% of the U.S. corn crop was used for ethanol and projections had ethanol's corn-use share rising rapidly, sparking concerns about unintended consequences of the policy-driven expansion of U.S. corn ethanol production. Dedicating an increasing share of the U.S. corn harvest to ethanol production evoked fears of higher prices for all grains and oilseeds that compete for the same land, higher livestock feed costs, higher food costs, and lower U.S. agricultural exports. In addition, several environmental concerns emerged regarding the expansion of corn production onto non-traditional lands, including native grass and prairie land. As a result of these concerns, policy makers sought to refocus biofuels policy initiatives in the 2008 farm bill (the Food, Conservation, and Energy Act of 2008, P.L. 110-246) in favor of non-corn feedstock, especially cellulosic-based feedstock.

Renewable energy policy in the 2008 farm bill became law six months after the enactment of the Energy Independence and Security Act of 2007 (EISA, P.L. 110-140). A key component of EISA was a significant expansion of the renewable fuels standard (RFS), which mandates the increasing use of "advanced biofuels" (i.e., non-corn starch biofuels), whose minimum use must grow from zero in 2008 to 21 million gallons by 2022.[13] The energy provisions of the 2008 farm bill were intended to reinforce EISA's program goals via a further refocusing of federal incentives toward non-corn sources of renewable energy.

2014 Farm Bill—Extends Most Programs with New Funding

All of the major farm bill energy programs from the 2008 farm bill expired at the end of FY2013 and lacked baseline funding going forward. The enacted 2014 farm bill (P.L. 113-79) extends most of the renewable energy provisions of the 2008 farm bill, with some notable exceptions. Key biofuels-related provisions in the enacted 2014 farm bill include

- §9002, which extends the bio-based marketing and federal bio-products certification programs to encourage federal procurement of bio-based products;
- §9003, which extends the Biorefinery Assistance Program with new funding;
- §9004, which extends the Repowering Assistance Program with new funding;
- §9005, which extends the Bioenergy Program for Advanced Biofuels with new funding;
- §9006, which extends the Biodiesel Fuel Education Program with new funding;
- §9007, which extends the Renewable Energy for America Program (REAP)— which provides support for rural energy efficiency and self-sufficiency and biofuels marketing infrastructure—with new funding, but includes a new provision which precludes the use of REAP funding for any mechanism for dispensing energy at the retail level—for example, blender pumps;
- §9008, which extends the Biomass Research and Development Initiative (BRDI) with new funding for biofuels research programs within USDA and the Department of Energy (DOE);
- §9009, which extends the Feedstock Flexibility Program;
- §9010, which extends the Biomass Crop Assistance Program (BCAP), including the Collection, Harvesting, Storage, and Transportation (CHST) component designed to incentivize the production of cellulosic ethanol feedstock;
- §9011, which repeals the Forest Biomass for Energy Program;

- §9012, which extends the Community Wood Energy Program with new funding;
- §9013, which repeals the Biofuels Infrastructure Study;
- §9014, which repeals the Renewable Fertilizer Study;
- §9015, which adds a new reporting requirement on energy use and efficiency at USDA facilities;
- §7212, which repeals the Agricultural Bioenergy Feedstock and Energy Efficiency Research and Extension Initiative; and
- §7526, which reauthorizes, with new funding, the Sun Grant Initiative programs that provide funding for competitive grants and coordinate research on advanced biofuels at land-grant universities and federally funded laboratories.

The 2014 farm bill excludes the Rural Energy Self-Sufficiency Initiative of the 2008 farm bill by omission. Each of the above-cited programs is described in detail in the section below entitled "Major Energy Provisions in the 2014 Farm Bill."

FUNDING FOR AGRICULTURE-BASED ENERGY PROGRAMS

In general, two types of funding are authorized by Congress in a farm bill—mandatory and discretionary. Some farm bill programs identified as receiving mandatory funds (including most of the bioenergy programs) are automatically funded at levels "authorized" in the farm bill unless Congress limits funding to a lower amount through the appropriations or legislative process. For many of these programs, mandatory funding is provided through the borrowing authority of USDA's Commodity Credit Corporation (CCC).[14] The farm bill may also specify some discretionary funding as "authorized to be appropriated"—such discretionary funding is actually determined each year through the annual appropriations process and may or may not reflect the funding level suggested in the authorizing legislation.

Funding under the 2008 Farm Bill

The 2008 farm bill authorized slightly over $1 billion in mandatory funding and $1.1 billion in discretionary appropriations to Title IX energy programs for FY2008-FY2012 (**Table A-6**). Mandatory authorizations included $320 million to the Biorefinery Assistance Program, $300 million to the Bioenergy Program for Advanced Biofuels, and $255 million to the Rural Energy for America Program (REAP). The Biomass Crop Assistance Program (BCAP) was authorized to receive such sums as necessary (i.e., funding is open-ended and depends on program participation); however, limits were later set on BCAP outlays under the annual appropriations process in FY2010, FY2011, and FY2012.[15]

The $1.1 billion of discretionary funding included $600 million for the Biorefinery Assistance Program. However, actual discretionary appropriations of $106 million through FY2012 to all Title IX energy programs were substantially below authorized levels.

As regards mandatory funding, all of the bioenergy provisions of Title IX—with the exception of Section 9010, the Feedstock Flexibility Program for Bioenergy Producers, which is authorized indefinitely—had mandatory funding only for the life of the 2008 farm bill, FY2008 through FY2012. As a result, all of the bioenergy provisions in Title IX of the 2008 farm bill, with the exception of the Feedstock Flexibility Program for Bioenergy Producers (Section 9010), expired on September 30, 2012.[16]

Funding under Continuing Resolutions for FY2013

The 112th Congress was unable to complete action on any of the regular FY2013 appropriations bills during 2012. Instead, a continuing resolution for the first half of FY2013 (CR, P.L. 112-175) was signed into law on September 28, 2012.[17] This was followed by a second CR to provide appropriations for the second half of FY2013 (P.L. 113-6).[18] The Rural Energy for America Program was the sole Title IX bioenergy program that received an appropriation of discretionary funds ($3.4 million) in FY2013.

Funding under ATRA—The 2008 Farm Bill Extension

Many of the 2008 farm bill programs were extended through September 30, 2013, by Section 701 of the American Taxpayer Relief Act of 2012 (ATRA; P.L. 112-240) signed into law by President Obama on January 2, 2013.[19] Under ATRA, discretionary funding was authorized to be appropriated at the rate that programs were funded under the 2008 farm bill.

Funding under the 2014 Farm Bill

The five-year reauthorization period (FY2014-FY2018) of the 2014 farm bill (P.L. 113-79) contains a total of $694 million in new mandatory funding and authorizes $765 million to be appropriated for the various farm bill renewable energy programs (**Table A-5**). Details are provided in the discussion of individual provisions below.

MAJOR ENERGY PROVISIONS IN THE 2014 FARM BILL

The following is a summary of the bioenergy-related authorities found in the 2014 farm bill, including (where applicable) a brief description of each program, funding levels, and the status of program implementation, including any noteworthy changes made by the 2014 farm bill.

Like the two preceding farm bills, the 2014 farm bill (P.L. 113-79) contains a distinct energy title (Title IX) that extends many of the previous bioenergy programs.[20] Four previous provisions are omitted or repealed, and a new provision, Section 9015, is added to require USDA to submit a report to the House and Senate Agriculture Committees on energy use and energy efficiency projects at USDA facilities. Two bioenergy-related provisions in the Research Title (Title VII)— one extended, one repealed—are also included in the following discussion.

TITLE IX—ENERGY PROVISIONS

Section 9001: Definitions

The 2014 farm bill made four substantive modifications to bioenergy related definitions as follows (7 U.S.C. §8101):

- **"biobased product"**—similar to prior law except for the explicit inclusion of forestry materials that meet biobased content requirements, notwithstanding the market share the product holds, the age of the product, or whether the market for the product is new or emerging;

- **"forest product"**—defined as a product made from materials derived from the practice of forestry or the management of growing timber including pulp, paper, paperboard, pellets, lumber, and wood products, and any recycled products derived from forest materials;
- **"renewable chemical"**—defined as a monomer, polymer, plastic, formulated product, or chemical substance produced from renewable biomass; and
- **"renewable energy system"**—a system that produces energy from a renewable source including distribution components necessary to move energy produced by such a system to the initial point of sale, but not any mechanism for dispensing energy at retail (e.g., a blender pump).

The first three modifications were designed to expand access to federal support for renewable energy to forestry products and renewable chemicals. The new definition for renewable energy systems was intended to prohibit REAP funds from being used for blender pumps.

Section 9002: Biobased Markets Program

Function: The 2008 farm bill renamed the federal biobased procurements preference program as the Biobased Markets Program. It requires federal agencies to establish a program with specifications for procuring biobased products including a national registry of biobased testing centers, and authorized a voluntary labeling program under which producers of biobased products may use the label "USDA Certified Biobased Product." (7 U.S.C. §8102)

Under the Biobased Markets Program, federal agencies and their contractors are required to purchase biobased products when the cumulative purchase price of procurement is more than $10,000 or when the quantities of functionally equivalent items purchased over the preceding fiscal year equaled $10,000 or more. Each federal agency and contractor must procure biobased products at the highest content levels within each product category unless the agency determines that the items are not reasonably available, fail to meet applicable performance standards, or are available only at an unreasonable price.

Administered by: Office of Energy Policy and New Uses (OEPNU), Office of the Chief Economist (OCE), USDA.[21]

Program History: The Biobased Markets Program was originally established under the 2002 farm bill as a federal procurement preference program that required federal agencies to purchase biobased products under certain conditions. USDA refers to the program as the BioPreferred® Program.[22] The final guidelines for the federal preferred procurement program were published on January 11, 2005 (70 *Fed. Reg.* 1792).[23] In addition to program guidelines, through June 11, 2013, USDA has promulgated 10 rounds of regulations for the BioPreferred® Program, designating 127 categories, with over 10,000 products qualifying for preferred federal procurement.[24]

The final rule for the voluntary labeling program for biobased products was published on January 20, 2011 (76 *Fed. Reg.* 3790).

Changes in 2014 Farm Bill: The 2014 farm bill (P.L. 113-79) extends the Biobased Markets Program through FY2018 while adding several new implementation requirements, including reporting of quantities and types of biobased purchases by federal agencies with a focus on biobased content requirements (explicitly including forest products); mandates (within one year of enactment) designation of intermediate ingredients or feedstocks and assembled and finished biobased products according to guidelines; adds auditing and compliance activities to ensure proper use of biobased labeling; mandates a study and report by USDA to assess economic impact of biobased product industry (due 180 days after enactment); and encourages expedited coordination, review, and approval (with appropriate technical assistance) of forest-related biobased products.

Funding: Under the 2014 farm bill, mandatory Commodity Credit Corporation (CCC) funding of $3 million for each of FY2014-FY2018 was authorized for biobased products testing and labeling. Discretionary funding of $2 million was authorized to be appropriated for each of FY2014-FY2018. However, no discretionary funding has ever been appropriated for the Biobased Markets Program through FY2013.

Under the 2008 farm bill, mandatory Commodity Credit Corporation (CCC) funding of $9 million was authorized—including $1 million for FY2008 and $2 million for each of FY2009- FY2012—for biobased products testing and labeling. Discretionary funding of $2 million was authorized to be appropriated for each of FY2009-FY2012.

Under ATRA, no new mandatory funding was included for the Biobased Markets Program, while discretionary funding of $2 million was authorized to be appropriated for FY2013. However, no appropriations were made to this program under either of the CRs for FY2013 (P.L. 112-175 or P.L. 113-6).

Section 9003: Biorefinery, Renewable Chemical, and Biobased Product Manufacturing Assistance Program

Function: Originally called the Biorefinery Assistance Program, this program assists in the development of new and emerging technologies for advanced biofuels.[25] Competitive grants and loan guarantees are available for construction and/or retrofitting of demonstration-scale biorefineries to demonstrate the commercial viability of one or more processes for converting renewable biomass to advanced biofuels. Biorefinery grants can provide for up to 30% of total project costs. Each loan guarantee is limited to $250 million or 80% of project cost. (7 U.S.C. §8103).

Administered by: Rural Business and Cooperative Service, Rural Development Agency (RDA), USDA, in consultation with DOE.

Program History: BAP was newly established under the 2008 farm bill. Mandatory funds are used for the loan guarantee portion of BAP, whereas discretionary appropriations are to be used to fund grants.[26] However, since Congress never appropriated any discretionary funds for BAP during the life of the 2008 farm bill, USDA has only moved forward with the loan guarantee portion of BAP.[27] The final rule for the BAP's guaranteed loans was published on February 14, 2011 (76 *Fed. Reg.* 8404). A correction was published on January 24, 2012 (77 *Fed. Reg.* 3379).

For loan guarantees, project lenders (not prospective borrowers) must submit the application.[28] Each loan guarantee application undergoes at least three rounds of review within USDA (including review by the Rural Development Agency, USDA; the National Renewable Energy Laboratory (NREL), DOE; and the Office of the Chief Economist (OCE), USDA). Average processing time per application is about nine months. Application fees include both a guarantee fee and an annual renewal fee.

Changes in 2014 Farm Bill: Renames the Biorefinery Assistance Program as the Biorefinery, Renewable Chemical, and Biobased Product Manufacturing Assistance Program. Funding for grants is eliminated. Also, P.L. 113-79 directs USDA to ensure diversity in types of projects approved and caps the funds used for loan guarantees to promote biobased product manufacturing at 15% of the total available mandatory funds.

Funding: Under the 2014 farm bill, mandatory CCC funding of $100 million in FY2014 and $50 million each for FY2015 and FY2016 (to remain available until expended) was authorized for loan guarantees. Thus, there is no new baseline funding after FY2016. Discretionary funding of $75 million annually was authorized for FY2014-FY2018.

Under the 2008 farm bill, mandatory CCC funding of $75 million in FY2009 and $245 million in FY2010 (to remain available until expended) was authorized for loan guarantees. Discretionary funding of $150 million annually was authorized for FY2009-FY2013 for grants under the 2008 farm bill and the ATRA extension. However, no discretionary funding was ever appropriated for BAP through FY2013. Any mandatory funding unspent from the FY2010 allocation of $245 million remained available through FY2013.

Section 9004: Repowering Assistance Program (RAP)

Function: The Repowering Assistance Program (RAP) makes payments to eligible biorefineries (i.e., those in existence on the date of enactment of the 2008 farm bill, June 18, 2008) to encourage the use of renewable biomass as a replacement for fossil fuels used to provide heat for processing or power in the operation of these eligible biorefineries.[29] Not more than 5% of the funds shall be made available to eligible producers with a refining capacity exceeding 150 million gallons of advanced biofuel per year. (7 U.S.C. §8104)

Administered by: Rural Business and Cooperative Service, RD, USDA.

Implementation Status: RAP was originally established under the 2002 farm bill as a grant program to help finance the cost of developing and constructing bio-refineries and biofuels production plants to carry out projects to demonstrate the commercial viability of converting biomass to fuels or chemicals.[30] The 2008 farm bill altered RAP's orientation to focus on converting fossil fuel burning plants to biomass or some other renewable fuel source for processing energy.

The proposed rule for the Repowering Assistance Program was published on April 16, 2010 (75 *Fed. Reg.* 20073). After a comment period and subsequent modifications, an interim rule was published on February 11, 2011 (76 *Fed. Reg.* 7916). Individual project awards are limited to $5 million or 50% of total eligible project costs, whichever is less.

Changes in 2014 Farm Bill: RAP was extended without changes to program implementation other than new funding levels.

Funding: Under the 2014 farm bill, mandatory CCC funding of $12 million for FY2014 was authorized under the 2014 farm bill, to remain available until expended (i.e., no new baseline funding after FY2014). Discretionary funding of $10 million annually for FY2014-FY2018 was authorized to be appropriated.

Under the 2008 farm bill, mandatory CCC funding of $35 million for FY2009 was authorized, to remain available until expended. Discretionary funding of $15 million annually for FY2009- FY2013 was authorized to be appropriated under the 2008 farm bill and the ATRA extension; however, only $15 million in FY2010 was appropriated through FY2013. No new mandatory funding was included for RAP under the ATRA farm bill extension; however, any mandatory funding unspent from the FY2009 allocation of $35 million remained available through FY2013.

Section 9005: Bioenergy Program for Advanced Biofuels

Function: The 2008 farm bill established a new Bioenergy Program for Advanced Biofuels to support and expand production of advanced biofuels—that is, fuel derived from renewable biomass other than corn kernel starch—by entering into contracts with advanced biofuel producers to pay them for production of eligible advanced biofuels.[31] The policy goal is to create long-term, sustained increases in advanced biofuels production. (7 U.S.C. §8105).

Administered by: Rural Business and Cooperative Service, RD, USDA.

Program History: Originally created by a 1999 executive order during the Clinton Administration, the bioenergy program provided mandatory CCC incentive payments to biofuels producers based on year-to-year increases in the quantity of biofuel produced. Under the 2002 farm bill, mandatory CCC funding of $150 million was available for each of FY2002 through FY2006; however, no funding was authorized for FY2007, effectively terminating the program.

The 2008 farm bill's Section 9005 revived the bioenergy program but refocused its funding to non-corn-starch biomass sources. Producers of advanced biofuels enter into contracts with USDA to receive payments based on the quantity and duration of production of advanced biofuels, the net renewable energy content of the biofuel, and other factors. Only one producer per refinery is eligible to apply. The interim rule for the Bioenergy Program for Advanced Biofuels was published on February 11, 2011 (76 *Fed. Reg.* 7936).

Producers must submit records to document their production of advanced biofuels. Payments will be made in two tiers. The first tier is based on actual production, while the second tier is based on incremental increases in production as an incentive to expand annual production on a sustained basis. Program funding is to be distributed according to the two tiers: in FY2010 the first tier received 80% of available funds and the second tier receives 20%; in FY2011 the first tier received 70%, the second tier 30%; in FY2012 the first tier received 60%, the second tier 40%; in FY2013 and beyond, each tier receives 50%. Payments are capped per recipient to ensure equitable distribution. Not more than 5% of the funds in any year can go to facilities with total refining capacity exceeding 150 million gallons per year. Solid advanced biofuels produced from forest biomass are ineligible for the second tier incremental payment and may not receive more than 5% of annual program funds.

Since the program's inception, more than $211 million in assistance payments have been provided to over 290 advanced biofuel producers in 47 states.[32]

Changes in 2014 Farm Bill: Extends the Bioenergy Program for Advanced Biofuels through FY2018 without changes to program implementation other than new funding levels.

Funding: Under the 2014 farm bill, mandatory CCC funding of $15 million for each of FY2014- FY2018 was authorized to remain available until expended. Discretionary funding of $20 million annually for FY2014-FY2018 was authorized to be appropriated under the 2014 farm bill. However, no discretionary funding has ever been appropriated for the Bioenergy Program for Advanced Biofuels program through FY2013.

Under the 2008 farm bill, mandatory CCC funding of $55 million for 2009, $55 million for FY2010, $85 million for FY2011, and $105 million for FY2012 was authorized to remain available until expended. Discretionary funding of $25 million annually for FY2009-FY2013 was authorized to be appropriated under the 2008 farm bill and the ATRA extension; however, no discretionary funding was appropriated through FY2013. In the final FY2012 Agriculture appropriations act (P.L. 112-55), mandatory spending was limited to $65 million.

Section 9006: Biodiesel Fuel Education Program

Function: The Biodiesel Fuel Education Program awards competitive grants to nonprofit organizations that educate governmental and private entities which operate vehicle fleets, and educates the public about the benefits of biodiesel fuel use. (7 U.S.C. §8106)

Administered by: National Institute of Food and Agriculture (NIFA) and Office of Energy Policy and New Uses (OEPNU), OCE, USDA.

Program History: Originally established under the 2002 farm bill, the Biodiesel Fuel Education Program was extended by both the 2008 and 2014 farm bills. The program is implemented by USDA through continuation grants. The final rule for the program was published on September 30, 2003 (68 *Fed. Reg.* 56137).

On July 15, 2003, USDA published a request for applications for the Biodiesel Fuel Education Program for FY2003 (68 *Fed. Reg.* 41770). USDA awarded the original program grants to two entities: the National Biodiesel Board and the University of Idaho. Under the 2008 farm bill, NIFA obligated its funding to the same two entities for an initial period of one year, but has agreed to support their efforts through FY2012 contingent on the satisfactory progress of this project. The program is monitored by the USDA Biodiesel Education Oversight Committee, which includes a DOE representative.

Changes in 2014 Farm Bill: Extends the Biodiesel Fuel Education Program through FY2018 without changes to program implementation other than new funding levels.

Funding: Under the 2014 farm bill, mandatory CCC funds of $1 million are provided annually for FY2014-FY2018; discretionary funds of $1 million each for FY2014-FY2018 are authorized for appropriation under the 2014 farm bill.

Under the 2008 farm bill, mandatory CCC funds of $1 million were provided annually for FY2008-FY2013 under the 2008 farm bill and the ATRA extension.

Section 9007: Rural Energy for America Program (REAP)

Function: REAP provides financial assistance for:

- grants, guaranteed loans, and combined grants and guaranteed loans for the development and construction of renewable energy systems (RES) and for energy efficiency improvement (EEI) projects (eligible entities include rural small businesses and agricultural producers);
- grants for conducting energy audits and for conducting renewable energy development assistance (eligible entities include state, tribe, or local governments; land-grant colleges and universities; rural electric cooperatives; and public power entities); and
- grants for conducting RES feasibility studies (eligible entities include rural small businesses and agricultural producers).

Renewable energy systems (RES) include those that generate energy from bioenergy (but excluding any mechanism for dispensing energy at retail—e.g., a blender pump), anaerobic digesters, geothermal, hydrogen, solar, wind, and hydropower. Energy-efficiency improvement (EEI) projects typically involve installing or upgrading equipment to significantly reduce energy use (7 U.S.C. §8107).

REAP is administered by the Rural Business and Cooperative Service, RD, USDA.[33]

Program History

The 2008 farm bill combined elements of two existing programs from the 2002 farm bill—the Energy Audit and Renewable Energy Development Program and the RES and EEI Program—into a single program renamed the Rural Energy for America Program (REAP). Certain provisions of REAP have been operating since 2005 under 7 C.F.R. part 4280, subpart B. Regulations for operating grants and loan guarantees under the 2002 farm bill's RES and EEI Program were published on July 18, 2005 (70 *Fed. Reg.* 41264). A series of *Federal Register* notices (cited below) were used to implement the REAP provisions in the 2008 farm bill (i.e., RES feasibility studies, energy audits, and renewable energy development assistance) until new regulations were implemented. On April 14, 2011, an interim rule for REAP was published (76 *Fed. Reg.* 21110) to consolidate the various REAP programs by including each part of the program in a single subpart based on USDA experience under the 2002 farm bill energy programs. The interim REAP rule includes several changes to previous implementation methods: both U.S. citizenship and the rural area location requirements were removed, and flexible fuel ("blender") pumps that dispense variable blends of petroleum and biofuels were included as viable renewable energy development projects. On April 12, 2013, USDA published a proposed rule for administering the grants and guaranteed loans program.[34]

During deliberations on the FY2012 Agriculture Appropriations Act (P.L. 112-55), the House had agreed, by a recorded vote of 283 to 128, to an amendment (H.Amdt. 475) to its version of the FY2012 appropriations act, H.R. 2112, that would have prohibited the use of funds for the construction of ethanol blender pumps or ethanol storage facilities. On June 16, 2011, the Senate considered a similar amendment (S.Amdt. 411) to separate, unrelated legislation (S. 782) that would have prohibited the use of REAP funds for the construction of ethanol blender pumps or ethanol storage facilities. However, the amendment was not agreed to in the full Senate by a 41- 59 vote.

Furthermore, the House prohibition on use of REAP funds for blender pumps or ethanol storage facilities was not included in the final FY2012 Agriculture Appropriations Act (P.L. 112- 55). However, by modifying the definition of a qualifying renewable energy system, the 2014 farm bill excludes blender pumps and any other mechanism for dispensing energy at retail from access to REAP funding.

According to USDA, more than 8,000 awards were made under REAP programs (and their predecessor) from FY2003 through FY2011, spanning all agricultural sectors in all states including more than $339 million in grants and $262 million in loan guarantees. During that period, REAP funds have helped more than 13,000 rural small businesses and agricultural producers and funded more than 1,000 solar projects and more than 560 wind projects.[35] See **Table A-4** for a list of USDA REAP funding notices.

Changes in 2014 Farm Bill: Extends REAP through FY2018, plus, adds new funding and a three-tiered application process with separate application processes for grants and loan guarantees for RES and EEI projects based on the project cost: tier-1 for projects < $80,000; tier-2 for projects > $80,000 but < $200,000; and tier-3 for projects > $200,000. In addition, a renewable energy system (RES) was redefined to exclude any mechanism for dispensing energy at retail— most notably blender pumps.

Funding: Under the 2014 farm bill, mandatory CCC funds of $50 million are authorized for FY2014 and each fiscal year thereafter (thus REAP's mandatory funding authority does not expire with the 2014 farm bill). Mandatory funds are to remain available until expended. Discretionary funding of $20 million annually was authorized to be appropriated for FY2014- FY2018.

Under the 2008 farm bill, mandatory CCC funds of $55 million in FY2009, $60 million in FY2010, $70 million in FY2011, and $70 million in FY2012 were authorized, to remain available until expended. Discretionary funding of $25 million annually was authorized to be appropriated for FY2009-FY2012. Actual discretionary appropriations were $5 million in FY2009, $40 million in FY2010, $5 million in FY2011, and $3.4 million in FY2012.

The FY2011 appropriations act (Department of Defense and Full-Year Continuing Appropriations Act, 2011; P.L. 112-10) reduced REAP discretionary funds from $25 million to $5 million, but left REAP's mandatory funding of $70 million intact. The FY2012 Agriculture Appropriations Act (P.L. 112-55) limited REAP mandatory spending to $22 million, while discretionary funding was authorized at $3.4 million, split evenly between grants and loan guarantees.

Under ATRA, no new mandatory funding was included for REAP; however, discretionary funding of $25 million was authorized to be appropriated for FY2013.

Section 9008: Biomass Research and Development Initiative (BRDI)

Function: BRDI—created originally under the Biomass Research and Development Act of 2000 (BRDA, P.L. 106-224)—provides competitive funding in the form of grants, contracts, and financial assistance for research, development, and demonstration of technologies and processes leading to significant commercial production of biofuels, biobased energy innovations, development of biobased feedstocks, biobased products, and other such related processes, including development of cost-competitive cellulosic ethanol. Eligibility is limited to institutions of higher learning, national laboratories, federal or state research agencies, private-sector entities, and nonprofit organizations.

BRDI provides for coordination of biomass research and development, including life-cycle analysis of biofuels, between USDA and DOE by creating the Biomass Research and Development Board to coordinate government activities in biomass research, and the Biomass Research and Development Technical Advisory Committee to advise on proposal direction and evaluation.[36] The 2008 farm bill moved BRDA in statute to Title IX of the 2008 farm bill and expanded the BRDI technical advisory committee. (7 U.S.C. §8108)

Administered by: National Institute of Food and Agriculture (NIFA), USDA, and DOE, jointly.

Program History: Since 2002 USDA and DOE jointly have announced annual solicitations and awards of funding allocations under BRDI.[37] Under the 2008 farm bill, applicants seeking BRDI funding must propose projects that integrate science and engineering research in the following three technical areas that are critical to the broader success of alternative biofuels production: feedstock development, biofuels and biobased products development, and biofuels development analysis. A minimum of 15% of funding must go to each area.[38] The minimum cost-share requirement for demonstration projects was increased to 50%, and for research projects to 20%.

From FY2002 through FY2010, more than $202 million was awarded to 110 projects, including $91.5 million from USDA and $111.1 million from DOE. During the FY2011 to FY2013 period, USDA announced another $103 million in awards to 17 additional projects.[39]

Changes in 2014 Farm Bill: Extends BRDI through FY2018 without changes to program implementation other than new funding levels.

Funding: The 2014 farm bill authorizes mandatory funding (to remain available until expended) of $3 million for four fiscal years—FY2014-FY2017—that is, baseline funding authority expires after FY2017. Discretionary funding of $20 million is authorized to be appropriated annually for FY2014-FY2018. However, no discretionary funding has ever been appropriated for BRDI through FY2013.

The 2008 farm bill authorized mandatory funding (to remain available until expended) of $20 million for FY2009, $28 million for FY2010, $30 million for FY2011, and $40 million for FY2012. Discretionary funding of $35 million was authorized to be appropriated annually for FY2009-FY2012. The FY2012 Agriculture appropriations act (P.L. 112-55) did not make any cuts to the $40 million in mandatory funding for BRDI.

Under ATRA, no new mandatory funding was included for BRDI; however, discretionary funding of $35 million was authorized to be appropriated for FY2013.

Section 9009: Feedstock Flexibility Program (FFP) for Bioenergy Producers

Function: The Feedstock Flexibility Program required that USDA establish (in FY2008) and administer a sugar-for-ethanol program using sugar intended for food use but deemed to be in surplus. USDA would subsidize the use of sugar for ethanol production through federal purchases of surplus sugar for resale to ethanol producers. USDA would implement the program only in those years where purchases are determined to be necessary to ensure that the sugar program operates at no cost to the federal government. (7 U.S.C. §8110)

The intent of the FFP is to provide the CCC a tool for avoiding sugar forfeitures. Under the sugar program, domestic sugar beet or sugarcane processors may borrow from the CCC, pledging their sugar production as collateral for any such loan, and then satisfy their loans either by repaying the loan on or before loan maturity or by transferring the title for the collateral to the CCC immediately following loan maturity, also known as "forfeiture" of collateral (as specified in 7 CFR 1435). The CCC is required to operate the sugar program, to the maximum extent practicable at no cost to the federal government, by avoiding forfeitures to CCC. If domestic sugar market conditions are such that market rates are less than forfeiture level (i.e., forfeitures appear likely), current law requires CCC to use FFP to purchase sugar and sell such sugar to bioenergy producers to avoid forfeitures.

Administered by: Farm Service Agency (FSA), USDA.

Program History: The FFP was implemented effective upon publication of the final rule by USDA in the *Federal Register* on July 29, 2013.[40] By late July 2013, U.S. sugar prices were below effective federal support levels, compelling USDA to activate FFP on August 15, 2013, and use an estimated $148 million of CCC funds to avoid possible sugar forfeitures.[41]

Changes in 2014 Farm Bill: Extends the Feedstock Flexibility Program through FY2018 with no changes to program implementation.

Funding: Under the 2014 farm bill, mandatory funding authority of such sums as necessary was extended through FY2018 by the 2014 farm bill. Under the 2008 farm bill, mandatory CCC funds of such sums as necessary were to be made available. Funding authority was extended through FY2013 by ATRA.

Section 9010: Biomass Crop Assistance Program (BCAP)

Function: The Biomass Crop Assistance Program (BCAP) provides financial assistance to owners and operators of agricultural land and non-industrial private forest land who wish to establish, produce, and deliver biomass feedstocks to eligible processing plants.[42] BCAP provides two categories of assistance:[43]

1. **establishment and annual payments**, including a one-time payment of up to 75% of the cost of establishment for perennial crops, and annual payments (i.e., rental rates based on a set of criteria) of up to 5 years for non-woody and 15 years for woody perennial biomass crops; and

2. **matching payments**, at a rate of $1 for each $1 per ton provided, up to $20 per ton, for a period of two years, which may be available to help eligible material owners with collection, harvest, storage, and transportation (CHST) of eligible material for use in a qualified biomass conversion facility.

Establishment and annual payments are available to certain producers who enter into contracts with USDA to produce eligible biomass crops on contract acres within designated BCAP project areas.[44] Eligible land for BCAP project area contracts includes agricultural land and nonindustrial private forestland, but does not include federal or state-owned land, land that is native sod. Lands enrolled in existing land retirement programs for conservation purposes—the Conservation Reserve Program (CRP) or the Agricultural Conservation Easement Program (ACEP)—also become eligible during the fiscal year that their land retirement contract expires. Generally, crops that receive payments under Title I (the commodity title) of the farm bill (e.g., corn, wheat, rice, and soybeans) and noxious weeds or invasive species are not eligible for annual payments.

Matching payments are available to eligible material owners who deliver eligible material to qualified biomass conversion facilities. Eligible material must be harvested directly from the land and separate from a higher-value product (e.g., Title I crops). Invasive and noxious species are considered eligible material and land ownership (private, state, federal, etc.) is not a limiting factor to receive matching payments. (7 U.S.C. §8111)

Administered by: Farm Service Agency (FSA), USDA.

Program History: On May 5, 2009, President Barack Obama issued a directive addressing a variety of advanced biofuel priorities including the implementation of matching payments for CHST of eligible materials for biomass conversion. On June 11, 2009, USDA published a NOFA (74 *Fed. Reg.* 27767) to implement the CHST matching payments component of BCAP. The NOFA was terminated on February 3, 2010, and, on February 8, 2010, USDA published a proposed rule for BCAP (75 *Fed. Reg.* 6264). The final rule was published on October 27, 2010 (74 *Fed. Reg.* 27767), and implements the full BCAP program, including the annual and establishment payment. USDA, as required by the 2008 farm bill, submitted a report to the House and Senate Agriculture Committees in February 2013 on the dissemination of the best practice data and information gathered from participants receiving assistance under BCAP.[45]

No BCAP payments were made in FY2008; however, through FY2012, nearly $900 million had been paid out to projects in 31 states.[46] As of June 2012, USDA had selected 11 BCAP project areas and continued to enroll producers for annual and establishment payments. However, due to the reduced funding availability imposed by limitations on the availability of mandatory funding through the annual appropriations process (see above discussion), USDA published an interim rule on September 15, 2011 (76 *Fed.*

Reg. 56949), amending the BCAP regulation to provide specifically for prioritizing limited program funds in favor of the "project area" portion of BCAP. The limited funding available for BCAP means that not all BCAP requests can be funded. The interim rule explicitly provides a priority for funding establishment and annual payments for project area activities because "such activities will produce the greatest long term good in BCAP by providing an ongoing supply of new biomass."[47] Under the interim rule, matching payments for CHST would be funded only if resources are available after funding all eligible project area applications. The interim rule also enables prioritization among project area proposals if eligible requests exceed available funding.

Changes in 2014 Farm Bill: Extends BCAP through FY2018. Changes enrolled land eligibility by including land under expiring CRP or ACEP easement contracts; includes residue from crops receiving Title I payments as eligible material, but extends exclusion to any whole grain from a Title I crop, as well as bagasse and algae. One-time establishment payments are limited to no more than 50% of cost of establishment, not to exceed $500 per acre ($750/acre for socially disadvantaged farmers or ranchers). CHST matching payments may not exceed $20 per dry ton (down from $45 per dry ton) and are available for a two-year period. CHST funding shall be available for technical assistance. Not less than 10% or more than 50% of funding may be used for CHST. Not later than four years after enactment of the 2014 farm bill, USDA shall submit to the House and Senate Agriculture Committees another report on best practices from participants receiving assistance under BCAP.

Funding: Under the 2014 farm bill, mandatory funding of $25 million was authorized for each of FY2014-FY2018. No discretionary funding was authorized. Under the 2008 farm bill, mandatory CCC funds of such sums as necessary were made available for each of FY2008-FY2012. Outlays were to depend on the number of participants. The 2010 Supplemental Appropriations Act (P.L. 111-212) limited BCAP funding to $552 million in FY2010 and $432 million in FY2011. The Department of Defense and Full-Year Continuing Appropriations Act, 2011 (P.L. 112-10), further reduced BCAP funding for FY2011 to $112 million.

With respect to FY2012 funding, the President's FY2012 budget proposed to limit funding for CHST to $70 million. The remaining annual and establishment payment portion of BCAP would remain at such sums as necessary (SSAN). On June 16, 2011, the House passed an FY2012 appropriations bill (H.R. 2112) that would have eliminated funding for BCAP for FY2012. In contrast, the Senate FY2012 spending bill left BCAP mandatory spending untouched. In the final FY2012 Agriculture Appropriations Act (P.L. 112-55), BCAP mandatory spending was limited to $17 million.

Under ATRA, no new mandatory funding was included for BCAP; however, discretionary funding of $20 million was authorized to be appropriated for FY2013.

Section 9011: Forest Biomass for Energy (Repealed)

Function: The Forest Biomass for Energy program is a research and development program to encourage use of forest biomass for energy. The Forest Service, other federal agencies, state and local governments, Indian tribes, land-grant colleges and universities, and private entities are eligible to compete for program funds. Priority is given to projects that use low-value forest byproduct biomass for the production of energy; develop processes to integrate bioenergy from forest biomass into existing manufacturing streams; develop new transportation fuels; and improve the growth and yield of trees for renewable energy. (7 U.S.C. §8112)

Administered by: Forest Service, USDA.

Program History: The Forest Service never announced any regulations for this program. The President's FY2011 and FY2012 budget proposed to fund both the Forest Biomass for Energy Program and the Community Wood Energy Program using funds from the Hazardous Fuels Program (Wildland Fire Management) within the Forest Service.

Changes in 2014 Farm Bill: The Forest Biomass for Energy program is repealed.

Funding: Program funding authority expired after FY2013. Under the 2008 farm bill, discretionary funding of $15 million annually was authorized to be appropriated for FY2009- FY2012. Under ATRA, discretionary funding of $15 million was authorized to be appropriated for FY2013; however, no funding was ever appropriated through FY2013.

Section 9012: Community Wood Energy Program

Function: The Community Wood Energy Program provides matching grants to state and local governments to acquire community wood energy systems for public buildings. Participants must also implement a community wood energy plan to meet energy needs with reduced carbon intensity through conservation, reduced costs, utilizing low-value wood sources, and increased awareness of energy consumption. (7 U.S.C. §8113)

Administered by: Forest Service, USDA.

Program History: The Forest Service has pursued the implementation of this program using funding from their overall State & Private appropriation.[48] An agency working group is developing the work plan for the Community Wood Energy Program, coordinating with Rural Development (RD) to ensure the new program is complementary with other biomass energy programs administered by RD. The President's FY2011 budget proposed to fund both the Forest Biomass for Energy Program and the Community Wood Energy Program using funds from the Hazardous Fuels Program (Wildland Fire Management) within the Forest Service. The President's FY2012 budget proposal included a similar request to fund both programs using the Hazardous Fuels Program—$15 million was requested for the Forest Biomass for Energy Program and $3.75 million for the Community Wood Energy Program.

Changes in 2014 Farm Bill: Extends the Community Wood Energy Program through FY2018; defines a Biomass Consumer Cooperative and authorizes grants of up to $50,000 to be made to establish or expand biomass consumer cooperatives that will provide consumers with services or discounts relating to the purchase of biomass heating systems or products (including their delivery and storage); and requires that any biomass consumer cooperative that receives a grant must match at least the equivalent of 50% of the funds toward the establishment or expansion of a biomass consumer cooperative.

Funding: Under the 2014 farm bill, discretionary funding of $5 million annually was authorized to be appropriated for FY2014-FY2018. No mandatory funding was included.

Under the 2008 farm bill, discretionary funding of $5 million annually was authorized to be appropriated for FY2009-FY2013. ATRA extended the program through FY2013 but no funding has been appropriated to date. However, the Forest Service awarded $49 million in funding from the American Recovery and Reinvestment Act of 2009 (ARRA, P.L. 111-5) for wood-to-energy projects, and the appropriations committee reports in FY2010 and FY2011 directed the use of $5 million in Hazardous Fuels funds for biomass energy projects.

Section 9013: Biofuels Infrastructure Study (Repealed)

Function: Section 9002 of the 2008 farm bill requested that USDA, DOE, EPA, and the Department of Transportation (DOT) jointly report on the infrastructure needs, requirements, and development approaches for expanding the domestic production, transportation, and distribution of biofuels given current and likely future market trends. A report including the study results was to be submitted to various related committees in Congress. No deadline was specified and the report was never undertaken.

Program History: No funding was ever appropriated for this activity.

Changes in 2014 Farm Bill: The Biofuels Infrastructure Study requirement is repealed.

Funding: Program funding authority expired after FY2013. Under the 2008 farm bill, no specific funding was announced for this study and no funding was ever authorized. In addition, no new funding authority was included in ATRA.

Section 9014: Renewable Fertilizer Study (Repealed)

Function: Section 9003 of the 2008 farm bill required that a report be submitted to the House and Senate Agriculture Committees within one year of receipt of the appropriations to carry out the study on the production of fertilizer from renewable energy sources in rural areas. The report was to be based on a study of the challenges to commercialization of rural fertilizer production from renewable sources, potential processes and technologies, and the potential impacts of renewable fertilizer on fossil fuel use and the environment.

Program History: This report was never undertaken.

Changes in 2014 Farm Bill: The Renewable Fertilizer Study requirement is repealed.

Funding: Program funding authority expired after FY2013. Under the 2008 farm bill, discretionary funding of $1 million was authorized to be appropriated for FY2009; however, no discretionary funding was ever authorized and no new funding authority was included in ATRA.

Section 9015: Energy Efficiency Report for USDA Facilities

Function: Within 180 days after enactment, USDA must submit a report to the House and Senate Agriculture Committees on energy use and energy efficiency projects at USDA facilities.

New Provision in 2014 Farm Bill: Requires a new report by USDA on energy use and energy efficiency projects at USDA facilities.

Funding: No specific funding was authorized for this study by the 2014 farm bill.

No Provision: Rural Energy Self-Sufficiency Initiative

Function: The Rural Energy Self-Sufficiency Initiative was designed to assist rural communities with community-wide energy systems that reduce conventional energy use and increase the use of energy from renewable sources. Grants are available to assess energy use in a rural community, evaluate ideas for reducing energy use, and develop and install integrated renewable energy systems. Grants are not to exceed 50% of the total cost of the activity. (7 U.S.C. §8109)

Administered by: Rural Business and Cooperative Service, RD, USDA.

Program History: Regulations were never announced for this program.

Changes in 2014 Farm Bill: No provision was included in the 2014 farm bill for the Rural Energy Self-Sufficiency Initiative; hence program funding authority expired after FY2013.

Funding: Program funding authority expired after FY2013. Under the 2008 farm bill and the ATRA extension, discretionary funding of $5 million annually was authorized to be appropriated for FY2009-FY2013; however, no funding was ever appropriated.

TITLE VII—ENERGY-RELATED AGRICULTURAL RESEARCH AND EXTENSION PROVISIONS

Three provisions from the Research title (Title VII) of the 2014 farm bill relate directly to renewable energy initiatives and are described here.

Section 7210: Nutrient Management Research and Extension Program (Repealed)

Function: This program provided research and extension grants for the purpose of finding innovative methods and technologies to allow agricultural operators to make use of animal waste, such as use as fertilizer, methane digestion, composting, and other useful byproducts. (7 U.S.C. §5925a)

Administered by: USDA.

Changes in 2014 Farm Bill: The 2014 farm bill repeals the Nutrient Management Research and Extension Program.

2014 Farm Bill Funding: No new funding since the program is repealed.

Section 7212: Agricultural Bioenergy Feedstock and Energy Efficiency Research and Extension Initiative (Repealed)

Function: Established for the purpose of using competitive grants to support research and extension activities that enhance the production of biomass energy crops and the energy efficiency of agricultural operations. (7 U.S.C. §5925e)

Administered by: USDA.

Changes in 2014 Farm Bill: The 2014 farm bill repeals the Agricultural Bioenergy Feedstock and Energy Efficiency Research and Extension Initiative.

2014 Farm Bill Funding: No new funding since the program is repealed.

Section 7516: Sun Grant Program

Function: The Sun Grant Initiative (SGI) is a national network of land-grant universities and federally funded laboratories—coordinated through regional Sun Grant centers—working together to further establish a biobased economy.[49] Competitive grants are available to land-grant schools within each region to be used towards integrated, multistate research, extension, and education programs on technology development and implementation. Sun Grant centers are also charged with reviving America's farming communities by placing an emphasis on rural economic development through the production of biobased renewable energy feedstocks.

A provision creating the Sun Grant Program was added subsequent to the 2002 farm bill under the Sun Grant Research Initiative Act of 2003 (Section 778, Consolidated Appropriations Act, 2004; P.L. 108-199). The initiative was originally established with five national Sun Grant research centers based at land-grant universities (a north-central center at South Dakota State University; a southeastern center at the University of Tennessee; a south-central center at Oklahoma State University; a western center at Oregon State University; and a northeastern center at Cornell University), each covering a different national region, to enhance coordination and collaboration among USDA, DOE, and land-grant universities in the development, distribution, and implementation of biobased energy technologies. The 2008 farm bill established a sixth regional center—a Western Insular Pacific Sub-Center at the University of Hawaii. The designation of specific universities as regional centers is removed by the 2014 farm bill. (7 U.S.C. §8114)

Administered by: NIFA, USDA. Each regional Sun Grant center manages the programs and activities within its region, although a process based on peer and merit review is used to administer grants.

Program History: As of October 2011, SGI had more than 130 field studies on biomass feedstocks currently underway with locations in more than 90% of the states.

Since NIFA has been assigned the authority to administer the program, awards made under the Sun Grant Program are subject to NIFA's assistance regulations at 7 C.F.R. part 3430 as announced on November 18, 2010 (Competitive and Noncompetitive Nonformula Federal Assistance Programs—Administrative Provisions for the Sun Grant Program, 75 *Fed. Reg.* 70578).

Changes in 2014 Farm Bill: The 2014 farm bill extends the Sun Grant Program with its current discretionary funding authority (i.e., subject to appropriations) of $75 million annually through FY2018. It also consolidates and amends the Sun Grant Program to expand input from other appropriate federal agencies and replace authority for gasification research with bioproducts research and makes the program competitive by removing designation of certain universities as regional centers.

Funding: Under the 2014 farm bill, discretionary funding of $75 million annually was authorized to be appropriated for FY2014-FY2018. Under the 2008 farm bill, discretionary funding of $75 million annually was authorized to be appropriated for FY2008-FY2012. However, only $2.25 million for FY2010 and $2.2 million for FY2012 were appropriated. No new funding authority was included in ATRA.

APPENDIX. SUPPLEMENTARY TABLES

Table A-1. Biorefinery Assistance Program: Notice of Funds Available (NOFA)

Fiscal Year	Federal Register	Date Announced	Amount	# of Projects Selected	Guaranteed Loan Value
2009	75 *Fed. Reg.* 70544	Nov. 20, 2008	$75 million	2[a]	$139 million
2010	75 *Fed. Reg.* 25076	May 6, 2010	$150 million	4[b]	$255 million
2011	76 *Fed. Reg.* 13351[c]	Mar. 11, 2011	$129 million	NA[d]	NA
2012	77 *Fed. Reg.* 4276	Jan. 27, 2012	$0	—	—
2013	78 *Fed. Reg.* 60822	Oct. 2, 2013	$76 million[e]	NA[f]	$181 million

Source: Federal Register.

Notes: Funding is for guaranteed loans. NA = not available.

[a] Initially three projects were selected; however, one was dropped due to ineligibility (a biodiesel retrofit project in Minnesota).

[b] Of the six current projects, four are cellulosic biofuel plants, one is an anaerobic digester, and one is an algae-to-diesel or jet fuel project.

[c] On June 6, 2011, an extension of the NOFA applications deadline to July 6, 2011, was published (76 Fed. Reg. 32355).

[d] As of the closing date for applications (July 6, 2011), USDA had received 13 applications valued at $1.3 billion in requested funding.

[e] Carry-over budget authority.

[f] Applications-for-funding deadline was January 30, 2014.

Table A-2. Repowering Assistance Program: Notice of Funds Available (NOFA)

Fiscal Year	Federal Register	Date Announced	Amount
2009	74 *Fed. Reg.* 28009	June 12, 2009	$20 million
2010	75 *Fed. Reg.* 24873	May 6, 2010	$8 million
2011	76 *Fed. Reg.* 13349	Mar. 11, 2011	$25 million
2012	77 *Fed. Reg.* 5232	Feb. 2, 2012	$25 million
2013	None	—	—

Source: Federal Register.

Notes: Funding is for guaranteed loans. NA = not available.

Table A-3. Bioenergy Program for Advanced Biofuels:
Notice of Contract Proposals

Fiscal Year	Federal Register	Date Announced	Amount
2009	74 *Fed. Reg.* 27998	June 12, 2009	$30 million
	75 *Fed. Reg.* 11836	Mar. 10, 2010	
2010	75 *Fed. Reg.* 24865	May 6, 2010	$80 million[a]
	76 *Fed. Reg.* 7966	Feb. 11, 2011	
2011	76 *Fed. Reg.* 13345	Mar. 11, 2011	$85 million
2012	77 *Fed. Reg.* 5229	Feb. 2, 2012	$25 million[b]
2013	78 *Fed. Reg.* 34975	June 11, 2013	$98.6 million[c]

Source: Federal Register.

Notes: Contract proposals (NOCPs) and awards to biorefineries for the production of advanced biofuels

[a] The initial FY2010 NOCP was for $40 million; however, this was was cancelled due to rural location and citizenship requirements. These requirements were removed in the interim rule of Feb. 11, 2011, and replaced with a new NOCP for $80 million.

[b] USDA announced that, although the 2008 farm bill provided $105 million in mandatory funding to support payments for advanced biofuels projects in FY2012, the FY2012 Appropriations Act imposed a limitation of $65 million that can be used for this program in FY2012. As a result, approximately $40 million of mandatory funding would be used to pay producers for FY2011 fourth quarter and other incremental payments.

[c] This amount includes FY2013 awards of $68.6 million and $30 million for production from prior fiscal years.

Table A-4. Rural Energy for America Program (REAP): NOSA & NOFA
Announcements

Fiscal Year	Federal Register			Amount ($ millions)		
	Type	#	Date	Total	Grant	Loan Guarantee
2009	NOSA	74 Fed. Reg. 10533	Mar. 11, 2009	$2.4	$2.4	$0
	NOSA	74 Fed. Reg. 24769	May 26, 2009	$60	$60	$0
2010	NOSA	75 Fed. Reg. 21584	Apr. 26, 2010	$88	Unspecified	Unspecified
	NOFA	75 Fed. Reg. 29706	May 27, 2010	$2.4	$2.4	$0
	NOFA	75 Fed. Reg. 47525	Aug. 6, 2010	$3	$3	$0

Table A-4. (Continued)

Fiscal Year	Federal Register			Amount ($ millions)		
	Type	#	Date	Total	Grant	Loan Guarantee
2011	NOFA	76 Fed. Reg. 20943	Apr. 14, 2011	$70	at least $42	remainder
2012	NOFA	77 Fed. Reg. 2948	Jan. 20, 2012	$25.4	at least $12.5	remainder
2013	NOFA	78 Fed. Reg. 19183	Mar. 29, 2013	$20.8	at least $10.4	remainder

Source: Federal Register.

Notes: NOSA = Notice of Solicitation of Applications; NOFA = Notice of Funds Available; NA

Table A-5. Authorized Funding for 2014 Farm Bill Title IX Energy Provisions, FY2014-FY2018 (budget authority in $ millions)

Section	Provision Name	Type[a]	FY 2014	FY 2015	FY 2016	FY 2017	FY 2018	Total FY14-FY18
§9002	Federal Biobased Markets Program	M	3	3	3	3	3	15
		D[b]	2	2	2	2	2	10
§9003	Biorefinery Assistance Program	M[c]	100	50	50	0	0	200
		D[b]	75	75	75	75	75	375
§9004	Repowering Assistance Program	M[c]	12	0	0	0	0	12
		D[b]	10	10	10	10	10	50
§9005	Bioenergy Program for Adv. Biofuels	M[c]	15	15	15	15	15	75
		D[b]	20	20	20	20	20	100
§9006	Biodiesel Fuel Education Program	M	1	1	1	1	1	5
		D[b]	1	1	1	1	1	5
§9007	Rural Energy for America Prog. (REAP)	M[c]	50	50	50	50	50	250
		D[b]	20	20	20	20	20	100
§9008	Biomass Research and Dev. Act (BRDA)	M[c]	3	3	3	3	0	12

Section	Provision Name	Type[a]	FY 2014	FY 2015	FY 2016	FY 2017	FY 2018	Total FY14-FY18
		D[b]	20	20	20	20	20	100
§9009	Feedstock Flexibility Prog. for Bioenergy Production[d]	M	SSAN[e]	SSAN	SSAN	SSAN	SSAN	SSAN
§9010	Biomass Crop Assistance Prog. (BCAP)	M	25	25	25	25	25	125
		D	0	0	0	0	0	0
§9012	Community Wood Energy Program	D[b]	5	5	5	5	5	25
§9015	Energy Efficiency Report for USDA facilities	Unfunded						
Total Mandatory Funding Authorized			209	147	147	97	94	694
Total Discretionary Funding Authorized			153	153	153	153	153	765

Source: P.L. 113-79 (Agricultural Act of 2014).

Notes: The following Title IX sections are unfunded repeals of programs from the 2008 farm bill: §9011, Forest Biomass for Energy; §9013, Biofuels Infrastructure Study; §9014, Renewable Fertilizer Study. The previous Rural Energy Self-Sufficiency Initiative was repealed by omission. In addition, three energy-related provisions from Title VII (Research, Extension, and Related Matters) were dealt with as follows: the Nutrient Management Research and Extension program was repealed by §7210, the Biofeedstock and Energy Efficiency Research and Extension Program was repealed by §7212, and the Sun Grant Program was extended (§7516) with authorization for discretionary funding of $75 million for each of FY2014-FY2018.

[a] M = mandatory funding; D = discretionary funding.

[b] In the past, many of the discretionary programs have never received any funding or received lesser amounts in the annual appropriations process than originally authorized in the farm bill.

[c] Mandatory funding is to remain available until expended for Title IX programs under the following provisions: §9003, §9004, §9005, §9007, and §9008.

[d] This program is triggered when a sugar surplus exists.

[e] SSAN = Such sums as necessary.

Table A-6. Authorized Funding for 2008 Farm Bill Title IX Energy Provisions, FY27008-FY2012[b]

(budget authority in $ millions)

Section[a]	Provision Name	Type	FY08	FY09	FY10	FY11	FY12	Total
§9002[a]	Federal Biobased Markets Program	Mand.	1	2	2	2	2	9
		Discr.[c]	0	2	2	2	2	8
§9003[a]	Biorefinery Assistance Program	Mand.	0	75	245	0	0	320
		Discr.[c]	0	150	150	150	150	600
§9004[a]	Repowering Assistance Program	Mand.	0	35	0	0	0	35
		Discr.[c]	0	15	15	15	15	60
§9005[a]	Bioenergy Program for Adv. Biofuels	Mand.	0	55	55	85	105	300
		Discr.[c]	0	25	25	25	25	100
§9006[a]	Biodiesel Fuel Education Program	Mand.	1	1	1	1	1	5
§9007[a]	Rural Energy for America Prog. (REAP)	Mand.	0	55	60	70	70	255
		Discr.[c]	0	25	25	25	25	100
§9008[a]	Biomass Research and Dev. Act (BRDA)	Mand.	0	20	28	30	40	118
		Discr.[c]	0	35	35	35	35	140
§9009[a]	Rural Energy Self-Sufficiency Initiative	Discr.[c]	0	5	5	5	5	20
§9010[a]	Feedstock Flex. Prog. for Bioenergy Prod.	Mand.	SSAN	SSAN	SSAN	SSAN	SSAN	SSAN
§9011[a]	Biomass Crop Assistance Prog. (BCAP)	Mand.	SSAN	SSAN	SSAN[d]	SSAN[d]	SSAN[d]	SSAN
§9012[a]	Forest Biomass for Energy	Discr.[c]	0	15	15	15	15	60

Section[a]	Provision Name	Type	FY08	FY09	FY10	FY11	FY12	Total
§9013[a]	Community Wood Energy Program	Discr.[c]	0	5	5	5	5	20
§9002	Biofuels Infrastructure Study	None	0	0	0	0	0	0
§9003	Renewable Fertilizer Study	Discr.[c]	0	1	0	0	0	1
Total Discretionary Funding Authorized[d]		0		278	277	277	277	1,109
Total Mandatory Funding Authorized		2		243	391	188	218	1,042

Source: P.L. 110-246 (Food, Conservation, and Energy Act of 2008) and P.L. 113-6 (Consolidated and Further Continuing Appropriations Act, 2013).

Notes: "SSAN" = Such sums as necessary.

[a] Section 9001 of the 2008 farm bill (P.L. 110-246) amends Title IX of the 2002 farm bill (P.L. 107-171). Sections 9001 through 9013 of the table are the amended section numbers.

[b] All mandatory funding authority expired at the end of FY2012, with the exception of the Feedstock Flexibility Program. Authority for discretionary funding was extended under the Continuing Resolution (P.L. 112-175), for the 1st half of FY2013 effective October 1, 2012, through March 27, 2013; the American Taxpayer Relief Act of 2012 (ATRA; P.L. 112-240, §701), and P.L. 113-6 (Consolidated and Further Continuing Appropriations Act, 2013) which appropriated funds for the 2nd half of FY2013.

[c] Many of the discretionary programs never received any funding or received lesser amounts through the annual appropriations process than originally authorized in the farm bill.

[d] The authority for funding under BCAP was reduced to 552 million in FY2010 and 432 million in FY2011 under the Supplemental Appropriations Act of 2010 (P.L. 111-212). BCAP funding for FY2011 was reduced a second time to 112 million under the Department of Defense and Full-Year Continuing Appropriations Act, 2011 (P.L. 112-10). Finally, the FY2012 Agriculture appropriations act (P.L. 112-55) reduced BCAP funding to 17 million for FY2012.

Table A-7. Title IX- Energy: Comparison of 2014 Farm Bill With Prior Law

Prior Law/Policy—Energy	Enacted 2014 Farm Bill (P.L. 113-79)
Definitions	
Advanced Biofuel. Fuel derived from renewable biomass other than corn kernel starch. Includes biofuel derived from sugar and starch other than corn kernel starch, renewable biodiesel, biogas produced from organic matter, as well as other fuels (e.g., home heating fuels, and aviation and jet fuels) from cellulosic biomass including organic waste material). *[7 U.S.C. 8101(3)]*	Same as prior law. *[Sec. 9001]*
Biobased Product. A commercial or industrial product—i.e., intermediate, feedstock, or end product (other than food or feed)— composed in whole or in part of biological products including renewable agricultural and forestry materials. *[7 U.S.C. 8101(4)]*	Same as prior law. *[Sec. 9001]*
Biofuel. A fuel derived from renewable biomass. *[7 U.S.C. 8101(5)]*	Same as prior law. *[Sec. 9001]*
Biomass Conversion Facility. A facility that converts renewable biomass into heat, power, biobased products, or advanced biofuels. *[7 U.S.C. 8101(6)]*	Same as prior law. *[Sec. 9001]*
Biorefinery. A facility (including equipment and processes) that converts renewable biomass into biofuels and biobased products, and may produce electricity. *[7 U.S.C. 8101(7)]*	Same as prior law. *[Sec. 9001]*

Prior Law/Policy—Energy	Enacted 2014 Farm Bill (P.L. 113-79)
No comparable provision.	**Forest Product.** A product made from materials derived from the practice of forestry or the management of growing timber including pulp, paper, paperboard, pellets, lumber, and wood products, and any recycled products derived from forest materials. *[Sec. 9001]*
Renewable Biomass. Includes- (A) materials, pre-commercial thinnings, or invasive species from National Forest System land and public lands that are: byproducts of designated preventive treatments (removed to reduce hazardous fuels, to reduce or to contain disease or insect infestation, or to restore ecosystem health), not used for higher value products, and harvested in accordance with applicable law and land management plans and requirements for old-growth maintenance, restoration, and management and large-tree retention, or (B) any organic matter available on a recurring basis from non-federal or Indian land including: renewable plant material (including agricultural commodities, plants and trees, and algae) and waste material (including crop residue, vegetative waste, wood waste and residues, animal waste and byproducts, and food and yard waste). *[7 U.S.C. 8101(12)]*	Same as prior law. *[Sec. 9001]*
No comparable definition.	Renewable Chemical. A monomer, polymer, plastic, formulated product, or chemical substance produced from renewable biomass. *[Sec. 9001]*

Table A-7. (Continued)

Prior Law/Policy—Energy	Enacted 2014 Farm Bill (P.L. 113-79)
Renewable Energy. Energy derived from a wind, solar, renewable biomass, ocean (including tidal, wave, current, and thermal), geothermal, or hydroelectric source. *[7 U.S.C. 8101(13)]*	Same as prior law. *[Sec. 9001]*
No comparable definition.	Renewable Energy System. A system that produces energy from a renewable source including distribution components necessary to move energy produced by such a system to the initial point of sale, but not any mechanism for dispensing energy at retail (e.g., a blender pump). *[Sec. 9001]*
Authorized Programs	
Biobased Markets Program. Requires federal agencies to purchase products with maximum biobased content subject to availability and flexibility and performance standards. Minimum biobased content standards applied to federal contracts on case-by-case basis. Continued voluntary labeling. Authorized mandatory funding of $1 million for FY2008 and $2 million annually for FY2009-FY2012; no mandatory funding was authorized for FY2013. Authorized to be appropriated $2 million annually for FY2009-FY2013 for testing and labeling. *[7 U.S.C. 8102]*	Extends the Biobased Markets Program through FY2018 including, in addition to preference for biobased products, establish a targeted biobased-only procurement requirement for federal agencies. Limits reporting on the availability, relative price, performance and environmental and public health benefits of biobased materials subject to the availability of data.

Prior Law/Policy—Energy	Enacted 2014 Farm Bill (P.L. 113-79)
	Adds reporting requirements of quantities and types of biobased products purchased by procuring federal agencies and a focus on biobased content requirements (explicitly including forest products). Mandates (within 1 year of enactment) designation of intermediate ingredients or feedstocks and assembled and finished biobased products according to guidelines. Adds auditing and compliance activities to ensure proper use of biobased labeling. Mandates study (and report) by USDA to assess economic impact of biobased product industry, due within one year of enactment. Encourages expedited coordination, review and approval (with appropriate technical assistance) of forest-related biobased products. Authorizes mandatory funding of $3 million annually for FY2014-FY2018. Authorizes to be appropriated $2 million annually for FY2014-FY2018. *[Sec. 9002]*

Table A-7. (Continued)

Prior Law/Policy—Energy	Enacted 2014 Farm Bill (P.L. 113-79)
Biorefinery Assistance Program. Assists in development of new and emerging technologies for advanced biofuels by providing competitive grants (up to 30% of total project costs) and loan guarantees (limited to $250 million or 80% of project cost) for construction and/or retrofitting of demonstration-scale biorefineries to demonstrate the commercial viability of one or more processes for converting renewable biomass to advanced biofuels. Provided mandatory funding of $75 million in FY2009 and $245 million in FY2010, available until expended, for loan guarantees. Authorized to be appropriated $150 million annually for FY2009-13 for grants. *[7 U.S.C. 8103]*	Renamed as the **Biorefinery, Renewable Chemical, and Biobased Product Manufacturing Assistance Program.** Extends and expands the program to include renewable chemical (as defined above in Sec. 9001) and biobased product manufacturing (defined as development, construction, and retrofitting of technologically new commercial-scale processing and manufacturing equipment and required facilities used to convert renewable chemicals and other biobased outputs into commercial-scale end products). Extends loan guarantee availability to the development and construction of renewable chemical and biobased product manufacturing facilities, directs USDA to ensure diversity in types of projects approved, and caps the funds used for loan guarantees to promote biobased product manufacturing at 15% of the total available mandatory funds. Eliminates grant funding.

Prior Law/Policy—Energy	Enacted 2014 Farm Bill (P.L. 113-79)
	Authorizes mandatory funding of $100 million for FY2014 and $50 million each for FY2015-FY2016 to remain available until expended, plus it authorizes to be appropriated $75 million for each of FY2014-FY2018. *[Sec. 9003]*
Repowering Assistance Program Provides funds to reduce or eliminate the use of fossil fuels for processing or power in biorefineries in existence at enactment. Not more than 5% of funds are available to eligible producers with a refining capacity exceeding 150 million gallons of advanced biofuel per year. Provided mandatory CCC funding of $35 million for FY2009, available until expended. Authorized to be appropriated $15 million annually for FY2009-FY2013. *[7 U.S.C. 8104]*	Extends prior law through FY2018. Authorizes mandatory funding of $12 million for FY2014, available until expended. Authorizes to be appropriated $10 million annually for FY2014-FY2018. *[Sec. 9004]*
Bioenergy Program for Advanced Biofuels. Provides payments to producers to support and expand production of advanced biofuels by entering into contracts to pay producers for production of eligible advanced biofuels. Provided mandatory funding of $55 million (FY2009), $55 million (FY2010), $85 million (FY2011), and $105 million (FY2012), available until expended. Authorized to be appropriated $25 million annually (FY2009-13) *[7 U.S.C. 8105]*	Extends the Bioenergy Program for Advanced Biofuels Program through FY2018. Authorizes mandatory funding of $15 million for each of FY2014-FY2018, available until expended. Authorizes to be appropriated $20 million annually for FY2014-FY2018. *[Sec. 9005]*
Biodiesel Fuel Education Program. Awards competitive grants to nonprofit organizations that educate fleet operators and the public on biodiesel benefits. Provided mandatory CCC funding of $1 million annually (FY2008-FY2012). Authorized to be appropriated $1 million for FY2013. *[7 U.S.C. 8106]*	Extends the Biodiesel Fuel Education Program through FY2018. Authorizes mandatory funding of $1 million annually for FY2014-FY2018. Authorizes to be appropriated $1 million annually for FY2014-FY2018. *[Sec. 9006]*

Table A-7. (Continued)

Prior Law/Policy—Energy	Enacted 2014 Farm Bill (P.L. 113-79)
Rural Energy for America Program (REAP). Provides financial assistance of grants, guaranteed loans, and combined grants and guaranteed loans for the development and construction of renewable energy systems (RES) and for energy efficiency improvement (EEI) projects (eligible entities include rural small businesses and agricultural producers); grants for conducting energy audits and for conducting renewable energy development assistance (eligible entities include state, tribe, or local governments, land-grant colleges and universities, rural electric cooperatives, and public power entities); and grants for conducting RES feasibility studies (eligible entities include rural small businesses and agricultural producers). Grants are limited to 25% of the cost of the RES or EEI activity. Loan guarantees are limited to a max of $25 million and a min of $5,000 up to 75% of the cost of a funded activity. Provides mandatory funds: $55 million (FY2009), $60 million (FY2010), $70 million (FY2011), and $70 million (FY2012), available until expended. Authorizes $25 million annually, subject to appropriations (FY2009-FY2013). *[7 U.S.C. 8107]*	Extends REAP through FY2018. Adds a council (as defined in section 1528 of the Agriculture and Food Act of 1981) as an eligible entity, Adds a 3-tiered application process with separate application processes for grants and loan guarantees for RES and EEI projects based on the project cost: tier-1 for projects < $80,000; tier-2 for $80,000 < projects < $200,000; and tier-3 for projects > $200,000. Mandatory funding of $50 million is authorized for FY2014 and each fiscal year thereafter, to remain available until expended. Authorizes to be appropriated $20 million annually for FY2014-FY2018. *[Sec. 9007]*

Prior Law/Policy—Energy	Enacted 2014 Farm Bill (P.L. 113-79)
Biomass Research & Development Initiative (BRDI). Provides competitive funding as grants, contracts, and financial assistance for research, development, and demonstration of technologies and processes leading to commercial production of biofuels and biobased products. Provides for coordination between USDA and DOE work related to biofuels and biobased products research and development programs through the Biomass Research and Development Board. Provides mandatory funding: $20 million (FY2009), $28 million (FY2010), $30 million (FY1022), and $40 million (FY2012). Authorizes to be appropriated $35 million annually (FY2009-FY2013). *[7 U.S.C. 8108]*	Extends BRDI through FY2018. Authorizes mandatory funding of $3 million annually for four fiscal years, FY2014-FY2017, to remain available until expended. Authorizes to be appropriated $20 million annually for FY2014-FY2018. *[Sec. 9008]*
Rural Energy Self-Sufficiency Initiative. Provides cost-share grants (up to 50%) for rural communities to assess energy systems and make improvements. Authorizes to be appropriated $5 million annually (FY2009-FY2013); however, no funds were ever appropriated and no rules were ever promulgated. *[7 U.S.C. 8109]*	No provision. Hence, program funding authority would expire after FY2013.
Feedstock Flexibility Program. Authorizes use of CCC funds (such sums as necessary) to purchase sugar (intended for food use but deemed to be in surplus) for resale as a biomass feedstock to produce bioenergy. USDA would implement the program only in those years where purchases are determined to be necessary to ensure that the sugar program operates at no cost to the federal government. *[7 U.S.C. 8110]*	Extends the Feedstock Flexibility Program through FY2018. *[Sec. 9009]*
Biomass Crop Assistance Program (BCAP). Provides financial assistance to owners and operators of agricultural land and nonindustrial private forest land who wish to establish, produce, and deliver biomass feedstocks under two categories of assistance:	Extends BCAP through FY2018. Changes enrolled land eligibility; includes residue from crops receiving Title I payments as eligible material, but extends exclusion to any whole

Table A-7. (Continued)

Prior Law/Policy—Energy	Enacted 2014 Farm Bill (P.L. 113-79)
(A) establishment and annual payments provided under contract between USDA and participating producers, including a one-time payment of up to 75% of cost of establishment for perennial crops, and annual payments (rental rates based on a set of criteria) of up to 5 years for non-woody and 15 years for woody perennial biomass crops, and (B) matching payments at a rate of $1 for each $1 per ton provided, up to $45 per ton, for a period of 2 years to help eligible material owners with collection, harvest, storage, and transportation (CHST) of eligible material for use in a qualified biomass conversion facility. Eligible material excludes Title I crops, animal waste and byproducts, food and yard waste, and algae. Provides mandatory CCC funding of such sums as necessary annually for FY2008-FY2012. Authorized to be appropriated $20 million for FY2013. *[7 U.S.C. 8111]*	grain from a Title I crop, as well as bagasse and algae. One-time establishment payments are limited to no more than 50% of cost of establishment, not to exceed $500 per acre ($750/acre for socially disadvantaged farmers or ranchers). CHST matching payments may not exceed $20 per dry ton but are available for a 2-year period. Not later than 4 years after enactment, USDA shall submit a report on best practice data and information gathered from participants. Also, it provides that funding under the subsection shall be available for technical assistance. Mandatory funding of $25 million is authorized for each of FY2014-FY2018. Not less than 10% or more than 50% of funding may be used for CHST. *[Sec. 9010]*
Forest Biomass for Energy Program. Requires the Forest Service to conduct a competitive research and development program to encourage use of forest biomass for energy. Authorized to be appropriated $15 million annually (FY2009-FY2013). *[7 U.S.C. 8112]*	Repeals the Forest Biomass for Energy Program. *[Sec. 9011]*

Prior Law/Policy—Energy	Enacted 2014 Farm Bill (P.L. 113-79)
Community Wood Energy Program. Provides grants of up to $50,000 for up to 50% of the cost for communities to plan and install wood energy systems in public buildings. The energy system acquired with grant funds shall not exceed an output of 50,000,000 Btu per hour for heating and 2 megawatts for electric power production. Authorized to be appropriated $5 million annually (FY2009-FY13). *[7 U.S.C. 8113]*	Extends the Community Wood Energy Program through FY2018. Defines Biomass Consumer Cooperative. Authorizes grants of up to $50,000 to be made to establish or expand biomass consumer cooperatives that will provide consumers with services or discounts relating to the purchase of biomass heating systems or products (including their delivery and storage). Any biomass consumer cooperative that receives a grant must match at least the equivalent of 50% of the funds toward the establishment of expansion of a biomass consumer cooperative. Authorizes to be appropriated $5 million annually for FY2014-FY2018. *[Sec. 9012]*
Biofuels Infrastructure Study. Required USDA to conduct a study (and report) to assess the infrastructure needs for expanding the domestic production, transport, and distribution of biofuels given current and likely future market trends with recommendations for such infrastructure through 2025 based on needs, costs, and other factors. No specific time frame or funding was provided. *[Sec. 9002 of P.L. 110-246]*	Repeals the requirement to conduct the study (and report). *[Sec. 9013]*

Table A-7. (Continued)

Prior Law/Policy—Energy	Enacted 2014 Farm Bill (P.L. 113-79)
Renewable Fertilizer Study. Required USDA to conduct a study to assess the current state of knowledge on the potential for the production of fertilizer from renewable energy sources in rural areas. Study was to be completed within one year of receiving an appropriation. Authorized to be appropriated $1 million for FY2009. *[Sec. 9003 of P.L. 110-246]*	Requirement to conduct the study is repealed. *[Sec. 9014]*
No comparable provision.	**Energy Efficiency Report for USDA Facilities.** Within 180 days after enactment, USDA is required to submit a report to the House and Senate Agriculture Committees on energy use and energy efficiency projects at USDA facilities. *[Sec. 9015]*

Source: Title IX- Energy, The Agricultural Act of 2014; P.L. 113-79.

Notes: For a comparison of prior and enacted law with the provisions in the House and Senate versions of the 2014 farm bill (i.e., the Senate-Passed S. 954 and the House-Passed H.R. 2642) see CRS Report R43076, *The 2014 Farm Bill (P.L. 113-79): Summary and Side-by-Side.*

End Notes

[1] For a list of federal incentives in support of biofuels production, see CRS Report R42566, *Alternative Fuel and Advanced Vehicle Technology Incentives: A Summary of Federal Programs*.

[2] See CRS Report R41282, *Agriculture-Based Biofuels: Overview and Emerging Issues*.

[3] CRS estimates based on ethanol production data, tax incentives, and congressional appropriations. These estimates do not account for the implicit subsidy inherent in biofuels import tariffs.

[4] See CRS Report R40155, *Renewable Fuel Standard (RFS): Overview and Issues*.

[5] For more information, see CRS Report R41282, *Agriculture-Based Biofuels: Overview and Emerging Issues*.

[6] For the origins and history of the import duty, see CRS Report R42566, *Alternative Fuel and Advanced Vehicle Technology Incentives: A Summary of Federal Programs*; for a discussion of exemptions from the import duty, see CRS Report RS21930, *Ethanol Imports and the Caribbean Basin Initiative (CBI)*.

[7] Most of these tax credits have expired. See CRS Report R42566, *Alternative Fuel and Advanced Vehicle Technology Incentives: A Summary of Federal Programs*, by Lynn J. Cunningham et al.

[8] For a complete listing of federal programs that support all types of renewable energy, see footnote 7.

[9] For information on state programs, see "Database of State Incentives for Renewables & Efficiency (DSIRE)," at http://www.dsireusa.org/index.cfm.

[10] For an overview of the 2002 farm bill's energy title, see CRS Report RL33037, *Previewing a 2007 Farm Bill*.

[11] For a discussion of the rapid growth of the U.S. biofuels sector, see CRS Report R41282, *Agriculture-Based Biofuels: Overview and Emerging Issues, Agriculture-Based Biofuels: Overview and Emerging Issues*.

[12] USDA, *World Agricultural Supply and Demand Estimates (WASDE) Report*, February 10, 2014.

[13] See CRS Report R40155, *Renewable Fuel Standard (RFS): Overview and Issues*.

[14] The CCC is the funding mechanism for the mandatory payments that are administered by various agencies of USDA, including all of the farm commodity price and income support programs and selected conservation programs. For more information on mandatory versus discretionary authorizations, see CRS Report R43110, *Agriculture and Related Agencies: FY2014 Appropriations*.

[15] See CRS Report *Biomass Crop Assistance Program (BCAP): Status and Issues*.

[16] For more information, see CRS Report R42442, *Expiration and Extension of the 2008 Farm Bill*.

[17] See CRS Report R42782, *FY2013 Continuing Resolutions: Analysis of Components and Congressional Action*.

[18] Consolidated and Further Continuing Appropriations Act, 2013, P.L. 113-6, March 26, 2013.

[19] A crop year refers to the year in which a commodity is harvested, and extends until the start of the succeeding year's harvest.

[20] For a side-by-side comparison of previous law with the energy provisions of the 2008 farm bill, see Table A-7 at the end of this report.

[21] The official USDA biobased markets program website is at http://www.biopreferred.gov/.

[22] OEPNU, OCE, USDA, *Metrics To Support Informed Decision Making for Consumers of Biobased Products*, by Marvin Duncan, Barbara C. Lippiatt, Zia Haq, Michael Wang, and Roger Conway, AIB No. 803, October 2008.

[23] This is an abridged citation for *Federal Register,* vol. 70, no. 7, pp. 1792-1812. This abridged format will be used throughout this report.

[24] Available at http://www.biopreferred.gov/ProductCategories.aspx.

[25] For more program information, see "Biorefinery Assistance Program," Business and Cooperative Programs (BCP), Rural Development (RD), USDA, at http://www.rurdev.usda.gov/BCP_Biorefinery.html.

[26] Based on information received by CRS from Kelly Oehler, Branch Chief, Energy Division, RD, USDA.

[27] See Table A-1 for a list of USDA BAP funding notices.

[28] More information on the BAP loan guarantee applications is available at http://www.rurdev.usda.gov/ SupportDocuments/BCP_9003_ApplicationGuide0311.doc.

[29] For more program information, see "Section 9004: Repowering Assistance Program," BCP, RD, USDA, at http://www.rurdev.usda.gov/BCP_RepoweringAssistance.html.

[30] See Table A-2 for a list of USDA RAP funding notices.

[31] For more program information, see "Section 9005: Bioenergy Program for Advanced Biofuels," BCP, RD, USDA, at http://www.rurdev.usda.gov/BCP_Biofuels.html.

[32] "USDA Announces Support for Producers of Advanced Biofuel," USDA News Release No. 0177.13, Sept. 12, 2013.

[33] See http://www.rurdev.usda.gov/BCP_Reap.html.

[34] USDA, "Rural Energy for America Program—Grants and Guaranteed Loans; Proposed Rule," *Federal Register,* Vol. 78, No. 71, April 12, 2013.

[35] USDA News Release No. 0099.12, March 20, 2012.

[36] For more information on the Biomass Research and Development Board, the Technical Advisory Committee, and project selection, visit http://www.usbiomassboard.gov/.

[37] For BRDI current FY2011 and historical (FY2002-FY2010) solicitations and awards visit http://www.usbiomassboard.gov/initiative/past_solicitations.html.

[38] For details on BRDI technical areas see http://www.nifa.usda.gov/nea /plants/in_focus /biobased_if_brdi.html.

[39] See USDA News Releases on Biomass Research and Development Grants dated: January 11, 2013; July 25, 2012, and May 5, 2011.

[40] "Sugar Program: Feedstock Flexibility Program for Bioenergy Producers," *Federal Register*, Vol. 78, No. 145, July 29, 2013.

[41] For more information see USDA, Economic Research Service (ERS), *Sugar and Sweeteners Outlook,* SSS-M-305, January 16, 2014, and CRS Report R42535, *Sugar Program: The Basics.*

[42] For more information, see CRS Report R41296, *Biomass Crop Assistance Program (BCAP): Status and Issues.*

[43] Farm Service Agency, USDA, "Biomass Crop Assistance Program (BCAP), "Fact Sheet," at http://www.fsa.usda.gov/Internet/FSA_File/bcap_update_may2011.pdf.

[44] See FSA, USDA, "BCAP Project Area Information," at http://www.fsa.usda.gov/FSA /webapp?area=home&subject= ener&topic=bcap-pjt.

[45] FSA, USDA, *BCAP: Biomass Crop Assistance Program: Energy Feedstocks From Farmers & Foresters,"* February 2013; available at https://www.fsa.usda.gov/Internet /FSA_File/bcap_ documentation.pdf

[46] For funding and other program details, see CRS Report R41296, *Biomass Crop Assistance Program (BCAP): Status and Issues*.

[47] *Federal Register*, Vol. 76, No. 179, Thursday, September 15, 2011, p. 56949.

[48] Farm Bill Working Group, Office of Budget and Program Analysis, USDA, "Highlights: Title IX-Energy," October 26, 2009.

[49] See "Sun Grant Initiative," at http://www.sungrant.org/.

In: The 2014 Farm Bill
Editor: Wilmer Combs

ISBN: 978-1-63321-432-3
© 2014 Nova Science Publishers, Inc.

Chapter 3

AGRICULTURE-BASED BIOFUELS: OVERVIEW AND EMERGING ISSUES[*]

Randy Schnepf

SUMMARY

Since the late 1970s, U.S. policymakers at both the federal and state levels have authorized a variety of incentives, regulations, and programs to encourage the production and use of agriculture-based biofuels—i.e., any fuel produced from biological materials. Initially, federal biofuels policies were developed to help kick-start the biofuels industry during its early development, when neither production capacity nor a market for the finished product was widely available. Federal policy (e.g., tax credits, import tariffs, grants, loans, and loan guarantees) has played a key role in helping to close the price gap between biofuels and cheaper petroleum fuels. Now, as the industry has evolved, other policy goals (e.g., national energy security, climate change concerns, support for rural economies) are cited by proponents as justification for continuing or enhancing federal policy support.

The U.S. biofuels sector responded to these government incentives by expanding output every year from 1980 through 2011 (with the exception of 1996), with important implications for the domestic and international food and

---

[*] This is an edited, reformatted and augmented version of the Congressional Research Service Publication, CRS Report for Congress R41282, dated May 1, 2013.

fuel sectors. Production of the primary U.S. biofuel, ethanol (derived from corn starch), has risen from about 175 million gallons in 1980 to nearly 14 billion gallons in 2011. U.S. biodiesel production (derived primarily from vegetable oil), albeit much smaller, has also shown strong growth, rising from 0.5 million gallons in 1999 to a record 969 million gallons in 2012. Despite the rapid growth of the past decades, total agriculture-based biofuels consumption accounted for only about 8% of U.S. transportation fuel consumption (9.7% of gasoline and 1.5% of diesel) in 2012.

Federal biofuels policies have had costs, including unintended market and environmental consequences and large federal outlays (estimated at $7.7 billion in 2011, but declining to $1.3 billion in 2012 with the expiration of the ethanol blender's tax credit). Despite the direct and indirect costs of federal biofuels policy and the relatively small role of biofuels as an energy source, the U.S. biofuels sector continues to push for federal involvement. But critics of federal policy intervention in the biofuels sector have also emerged. Current issues and policy developments related to the U.S. biofuels sector that are of interest to Congress include

- Many federal biofuels policies require routine congressional monitoring and occasional reconsideration in the form of reauthorization or new appropriations.
- The 10% ethanol-to-gasoline blend ratio—known as the "blend wall"—poses a barrier to expansion of ethanol use. The Environmental Protection Agency (EPA) issued waivers to allow ethanol blending of up to 15% (per gallon of gasoline) for use in model year 2001 and newer light-duty motor vehicles. However, the limitation to newer vehicles, coupled with infrastructure issues, could limit rapid expansion of blending rates.
- The slow development of cellulosic biofuels has raised concerns about the industry's ability to meet large federal usage mandates, which in turn has raised the potential for future EPA waivers of mandated biofuel volumes and has contributed to a cycle of slow investment in and development of the sector.

In 2012, the expiration of the blender tax credit, poor profit margins (due primarily to high corn prices), and the emerging blend wall limitation have contributed to a drop-off in ethanol production and have generated considerable uncertainty about the ethanol industry's future.

INTRODUCTION

Increasing dependence on foreign sources of crude oil, concerns over global climate change, and the desire to promote domestic rural economies have raised interest in renewable biofuels as an alternative to petroleum in the U.S. transportation sector. However, energy from renewable sources has historically been more expensive to produce and use than fossil-fuel-based energy.[1] U.S. policymakers have attempted to overcome this economic impediment by enacting an increasing number of policies since the late 1970s, at both the state and federal levels, to directly support U.S. biofuels production and use. Policy measures have included blending and production tax credits to lower the cost of biofuels to end users, an import tariff to protect domestic ethanol from cheaper foreign-produced ethanol, research grants to stimulate the development of new technologies, loans and loan guarantees to facilitate the development of biofuels production and distribution infrastructure, and, perhaps most importantly, minimum usage requirements to guarantee a market for biofuels irrespective of their cost.[2]

This report describes agriculture-based biofuels and the evolution of the U.S. biofuels sector with a focus on the role that federal policy has played in shaping its development.[3] In addition, it highlights emerging issues that are critical to the biofuels sector and of relevance to Congress.

BIOFUELS DEFINED

Any fuel produced from biological materials—whether burned for heat or processed into alcohol—qualifies as a "biofuel." The term is most often used to refer to liquid transportation fuels produced from some type of biomass. The two principal biofuels are ethanol and biodiesel; however, other fuels such as methanol and butanol could also qualify when produced from a qualifying biomass.

Biomass is organic matter that can be converted into energy. Common examples of biomass include food crops, energy crops (e.g., switchgrass or prairie perennials), crop residues, wood waste and byproducts, and animal manure. The term biomass has been a part of legislation enacted by Congress for various programs over the past 30 years; however, its explicit definition has evolved with shifting policy objectives.[4] Over the last few years, the concept of biomass has grown to include such diverse sources as algae, construction debris, municipal solid waste, yard waste, and food waste. The exact definition of biomass is critical, since it determines which feedstocks and resultant biofuels qualify for the different federal biofuels programs.

For example, the principal biofuels program in effect as of this report is the Renewable Fuels Standard (RFS), which mandates annual usage rates for four nested categories of biofuels—(1) total renewable fuels, (2) advanced renewable fuels, (3) cellulosic biofuel, and (4) biomass-based diesel.[5] Qualifying biofuels under each category are differentiated by their type of feedstock, the land on which the feedstock is produced (e.g., federal versus private, virgin versus previously cultivated soil, etc.), the production process used both to grow the feedstock and to process it into a biofuel (certain technologies are favored based primarily on environmental considerations), and the estimated amount of greenhouse gas emissions that result from the entire production pathway.

The idea of formally defining biomass has evoked criticism. Some argue that by explicitly enunciating qualifying feedstocks, the definition may be excluding new or as-yet-undiscovered feedstocks that may emerge in the future. Also, there appears to be some inconsistency across programs. For example, algae-based biofuels presently do not qualify for inclusion under the RFS cellulosic biofuels mandate, but do qualify for the "advanced other" biofuels mandate, as well as for the cellulosic biofuels tax credit and the depreciation allowance for qualifying cellulosic biofuels plants.[6] These differentiations tend to confuse and may slow or inhibit investments in algae-based biofuels.

Ethanol from Corn Starch Dominates U.S. Biofuels Production

Ethanol is the principal biofuel produced in the United States (**Figure 1**). Ethanol, or ethyl alcohol, is an alcohol made by fermenting and distilling simple sugars. As a result, ethanol can be produced from any biological feedstock that contains appreciable amounts of sugar or materials that can be converted into sugar such as starch or cellulose. Sugar beets and sugar cane are examples of feedstock that contain sugar. Corn contains starch that can relatively easily be converted into sugar. Trees, grasses, and most agricultural and municipal wastes are made up of a significant percentage of cellulose, which can also be converted to sugar, although with more difficulty than is required to convert starch.

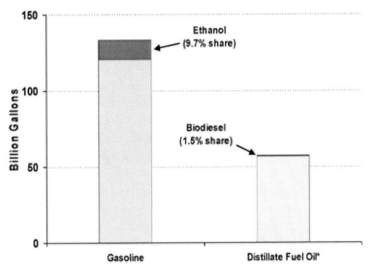

Sources: Calculated by CRS based on data from the Energy Information Agency (EIA), Department of Energy (DOE), *Monthly Energy Review*, March 2013: ethanol from Table 10.3, biodiesel from Table 10.4, and gasoline and distillate fuel oil use from Table 3.5.

Note: All data are in actual volumes; i.e., there is no conversion for gasoline energy equivalency. Distillate fuel oil includes both transportation and home heating oil uses.

Figure 1. Ethanol Had Nearly a 10% Share of U.S. Motor Gasoline Fuel Use in 2012.

Since its development in the late 1970s, U.S. biofuels output has relied almost exclusively on ethanol produced from corn starch. Small amounts of ethanol have also been produced using sorghum, wheat, barley, and brewery waste. This contrasts with Brazil, the world's second-largest ethanol producer behind the United States, where sugar cane is the principal feedstock. In 2012, the United States and Brazil accounted for 88% of the world's ethanol production.[7] Approximately 13.3 billion gallons of ethanol were produced in the United States in 2012, over 95% from corn starch.

Because of concerns over the significant expansion in corn production for use as an ethanol feedstock, interest has grown in spurring the development of motor fuels produced from cellulosic biomass materials. Since these biomass sources do not compete with traditional food and feed crops for prime cropland, it is thought that their use would result in substantially fewer unintended market effects. However, the technology needed for the conversion of cellulose into its constituent sugars before conversion to biofuels, while successful in laboratory settings, is thought to be expensive relative to corn ethanol and has yet to be replicated on a significant commercial scale.[8] Many uncertainties remain concerning both the viability and the speed of commercial development of cellulosic biofuels.[9]

After ethanol, biodiesel is the next most significant biofuel in the United States. Biodiesel is an alternative diesel fuel that can be produced from any type of organic-based oil, including vegetable oils, animal fats, and waste restaurant grease and oils. In the United States and Brazil, biodiesel has traditionally been made from soybean oil. In the European Union, rapeseed oil is the primary feedstock, while Canada relies primarily on canola oil. In recent years persistently high vegetable oil prices have pushed biodiesel producers to increase the share of much cheaper animal fats (especially poultry fat) and tropical palm oil; however, soybean oil remains the largest single source of biodiesel feedstock in the United States, with a share of over 56% in 2012.[10]

Other biofuels with the potential to play a role in the U.S. market include diesel fuel substitutes and other alcohols (e.g., methanol and butanol) produced from biomass.

Biofuels Value Determinants

The value of a biofuel is determined by its end use. Ethanol is primarily used as a substitute for gasoline; however, it has some additional properties (i.e., as an oxygenate and an octane enhancer) that provide value as a gasoline additive. Biodiesel's primary use is as a substitute for petroleum-based diesel transportation fuel; however, biodiesel can also be used as a direct substitute for home heating oil and as a blend in jet fuel. Also, both ethanol and biodiesel may derive additional value as an additive to meet federal usage mandates under the Renewable Fuel Standard (RFS) depending on market conditions.

The Renewable Fuel Standard (RFS)[11]

The RFS requires the blending of renewable fuels (including ethanol and biodiesel) in U.S. transportation fuel. The RFS includes specific quotas for total renewable biofuels, as well as nested subcategories for advanced biofuels (i.e., non-corn-starch ethanol), cellulosic biofuels, and biomass-based diesel fuel. The RFS also includes a cap on the eligible volume of corn-starch ethanol.[12] The RFS is administered by EPA. Qualifying biofuels must meet explicit criteria on lifecycle greenhouse gas (GHG) emissions[13] and feedstock production pathways (including restrictions on the land on which feedstocks are produced, feedstock production methods, and the biofuels plant processing technology).

Federal policy that mandates the use of a minimum volume of biofuel creates a source of demand that is not based on price, but rather on government fiat. As long as the consumption of biofuels is less than the mandated volume, its use is obligatory.

Ethanol Sources of Demand

With respect to ethanol, there is no difference to the end user between corn-starch ethanol, sugarcane ethanol, and cellulosic ethanol, although their production processes differ substantially in terms of feedstock, technology, and cost. As a result, all three share the same value determinants. In the presence of government policy, demand for ethanol derives from four potential uses:

- as an oxygenate additive in gasoline to help improve engine combustion and cleaner burning of fuel;
- as an additive to gasoline to enhance its octane level and engine performance;[14]
- as an additive to gasoline at blend ratios of up to 10% ethanol and 90% gasoline (known as E10), to meet federally mandated minimum usage requirements under one of the RFS categories for qualifying ethanol biofuels;[15] or
- as a substitute for gasoline at ethanol-to-gasoline blend ratios greater than E10.

Biodiesel Sources of Demand

In the presence of government policy, demand for biodiesel derives from the following potential uses:

- as a substitute for petroleum-based diesel transportation fuel;
- as a substitute for home heating oil;
- as a blend in jet fuel; and
- as an additive to petroleum-based diesel to meet federally mandated minimum usage requirements under one of the RFS categories for qualifying biofuels.[16]

Biofuel Supply Relative to RFS Mandates Affects Valuation

Depending on the relationship between the RFS mandate (blending demand) and the available supply (production plus imports) of qualifying biofuels, different RFS biofuels categories may have significantly different valuations, as greater scarcity will lead to greater value.

Under the RFS, each gallon of qualifying biofuel has an associated renewable identification number (RIN) that is detached at point of blending and submitted to the EPA as proof of fulfilling that year's RFS usage requirement for a specific biofuel category.[17] When a specific biofuel is blended (or used) in excess of its RFS mandate, the surplus RINs may be sold (ideally to another fuel blender to make up for a shortfall in meeting that blender's own RFS mandate) or stored for use in meeting the following year's RFS mandate. As a result of their tradability, secondary markets for RINs—by RFS category—have developed and gain in importance whenever the supply of a specific biofuel type tightens relative to its RFS mandate. RIN values are nested— since cellulosic and biomass-based diesel RINs can be used to meet their own category as well as the advanced and total categories, they have an inherent premium over advanced and total RINs. Similarly, advanced RINs would have a premium over total RINs.

In contrast, when the supply of a specific biofuels category exceeds its mandated usage volume, the associated "nested" value will diminish. In volumes above the RFS total renewable mandate, biofuels use is no longer obligatory and it must compete directly in the marketplace with its petroleum-based counterpart. As a result, once they have met their RFS blending mandates, fuel blenders, seeking to maximize their profits, are very sensitive to price relationships between petroleum-based fuels and biofuels. This is particularly important for ethanol since it contains only about 68% of the energy content of gasoline. As a result, value-conscious consumers could be expected to willingly pay only about 68% of the price of gasoline for ethanol.

From 2006—when the RFS was first introduced—through 2011, both ethanol production capacity, supply (production and imports combined), and consumption have easily exceeded the federally mandated usage levels (**Figure 2**).[18] As a result, ethanol's marginal value during that period was as a transportation fuel (rather than as an additive), where it competed directly with gasoline. However, economic conditions changed substantially in 2012, driven largely by the severe drought that summer, and the RFS has played a larger role in driving ethanol use. As for biodiesel, which is significantly more expensive to produce than its petroleum-based counterpart, biodiesel's use has been driven almost entirely by federal policy—i.e., the RFS biomass-based diesel and the biodiesel production tax credit (described below).

Blend Wall Emerges as Major Value Determinant

An important valuation concern for U.S. ethanol consumption in 2013 is the emergence of the so-called "blend wall" as a constraint on domestic consumption of ethanol in sufficient volumes to satisfy the RFS mandate. Ethanol-gasoline blends of up to 10% ethanol are compatible with existing vehicles and infrastructure (fuel tanks, retail pumps, delivery infrastructure, etc.). All automakers that produce cars and light trucks for the U.S. market warranty their vehicles to run on gasoline with up to 10% ethanol (E10); however, automakers have been reluctant to offer such warranties for higher ethanol blend ratios. As a result, the 10% blend ratio represents an upper bound (sometimes referred to as the "blend wall") to the amount of ethanol that can be introduced into the gasoline pool given the current automobile fleet and fuel delivery infrastructure. In 2012, ethanol accounted for nearly a 10% share of blended gasoline sold in the United States (**Figure 1**). In 2013, the RFS mandates for non-advanced ethanol of 13.8 bgals will likely exceed the blend wall (estimated at approximately 13 bgals by CRS based on EIA data). Supplementing actual ethanol blending with carry-over RINs (estimated at 2.6 bgals) will likely be sufficient to satisfy the 2013 RFS; however, surmounting the blend wall could prove more difficult in 2014.[19] Because of this infrastructure constraint, ethanol production in excess of the blend wall will have limited value in the domestic market unless it is consumed at higher blending ratios in flex-fuel vehicles (FFVs) or exported into the international market.[20]

EVOLUTION OF THE U.S. ETHANOL SECTOR

Federal Policy Kick-Starts Ethanol Production

Several events contributed to the startup and growth of U.S. ethanol production in the late 1970s. First, the global energy crises of the early and late 1970s provided the rationale for a federal policy initiative aimed at promoting energy independence from foreign crude oil sources. In response, the U.S. Congress established a partial exemption for ethanol from the motor fuels excise tax (legislated as part of the Energy Tax Act of 1978). All ethanol blended in the United States—whether imported or produced domestically—

was eligible for a \$0.40 per gallon tax credit. In 1980, an import duty for fuel ethanol was established by the Omnibus Reconciliation Act of 1980 (P.L. 96-499) to offset the domestic tax credit being applied to foreign-sourced ethanol.

As U.S. ethanol production began to emerge in the 1980s, ethanol became recognized as a gasoline oxygenate. The Deficit Reduction Act of 1984 raised the ethanol tax credit to \$0.60 per gallon.[21] Based on its oxygenate characteristic, provisions of the Clean Air Act Amendments of 1990 (CAAA90) favored ethanol blending with reformulated gasoline (RFG).[22] One of the requirements of RFG specified by CAAA90 was a 2% oxygen requirement, which was met by blending "oxygenates," including methyl tertiary butyl ether (MTBE) and ethanol into the gasoline.[23] Ethanol was the preferred oxygenate in the Midwest where it was produced, while MTBE—a petroleum derivative—was used in almost all RFG outside of the Midwest.

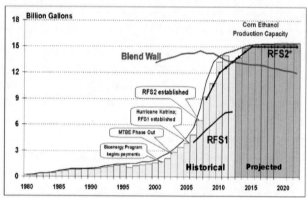

Source: Ethanol consumption historical data for 1980-2012 is from EIA, *Monthly Energy Review*, March 2013, Table 3.5; blend wall historical and projected data are calculated by CRS based on the EIA, DOE, data found in the AEO *Annual Energy Outlook* 2013. Projections for 2013-2022 are corn ethanol production from FAPRI, *FAPRI- MU Biofuel Baseline*, FAPRI-MU Report #02-13, March 2013. The projection data exclude ethanol production from advanced sources, e.g., cellulosic or sugarcane.

Note: RFS2* shown in the chart represents the non-advanced component (RFS code D6) equal to the total renewable fuel mandate minus the advanced biofuel mandate, and roughly approximates the cap on qualifying corn-starch ethanol consumption; ethanol from advanced sources are excluded from this data and this chart. Achieving the corn ethanol consumption levels in excess of the blend wall (as portrayed in this chart and described later in the text) would necessitate substantial consumption at higher blends such as E15 or E85.

Figure 2. U.S. Corn Ethanol Consumption, RFS, and Blend Wall, 1980 to 2022.

In addition to CAAA90 oxygenate requirements, a tax credit for small ethanol producer was established in 1990 (Omnibus Budget Reconciliation Act of 1990; P.L. 101-508) as a $0.10 per gallon supplement to the existing ethanol tax credit, but limited to the first 15 million gallons of ethanol produced by ethanol producers with production capacity below 30 million gallons per year.[24]

Aided by these events, the U.S. ethanol industry steadily grew during its first two decades—rising from an estimated 175 million gallons in 1980 to 1.8 billion gallons in 2001, when ethanol production was using about 7% of the U.S. corn crop.

Government Role Has Grown Since 2000

The first decade of the 2000s experienced a substantial increase in federal involvement in the U.S. biofuels sector. In FY2001, the Bioenergy Program[25] began making payments from the U.S. Department of Agriculture's (USDA's) Commodity Credit Corporation (CCC)[26] to eligible biofuel producers—ethanol and biodiesel—based on any year-to-year increases in the quantity of biofuels produced.

The Bioenergy Program was instituted by USDA because the program's principal goal was to encourage greater purchases of eligible farm commodities used in the production of biofuels (e.g., corn for ethanol or soybean oil for biodiesel).

The executive order creating the Bioenergy Program was followed by a series of legislation containing various provisions that further aided the U.S. biofuels industry. The first of these new laws—the Biomass Research and Development Act of 2000 (Biomass Act; Title III, P.L. 106- 224)—contained several provisions to expand research and development in the area of biomass-based renewable fuel production.

The 2002 farm bill (P.L. 107-171) included several biofuels programs spread across three separate titles—Title II: Conservation, Title VI: Rural Development, and Title IX: Energy (the first-ever energy title in a farm bill). Each title contained programs that encouraged the research, production, and use of renewable fuels such as ethanol, biodiesel, anaerobic digesters, and wind energy systems.

In addition, Section 9010 of Title IX codified and extended the Bioenergy Program and its funding by providing that $150 million would be available annually through the CCC for FY2003-FY2006.[27]

The Healthy Forests Restoration Act of 2003 (P.L. 108-148) amended the Biomass Act of 2000 by expanding the use of grants, contracts, and assistance for biomass to include a broader range of forest management activities. It also expanded funding availability of programs established by the Biomass Act and the 2002 farm bill, and it established a program to accelerate adoption of biomass-related technologies through community-based marketing and demonstration activities, and to establish small-scale businesses to use biomass materials.

The American Jobs Creation Act of 2004 (P.L. 108-357) contained a provision (Section 301) that replaced the existing tax exemptions for alcohol fuels (i.e., ethanol) with an excise tax credit of $0.51 per gallon. This act also extended the small ethanol producer tax credit.

MTBE Phase-Out Enhances Ethanol's Value

In addition to a growing list of federal and state policies, the U.S. biofuels industry received an additional boost in the early 2000s with the emergence of water contamination problems associated with underground MTBE storage tanks in several locations scattered throughout the country. MTBE was thought to be a possible carcinogen and, as a result, posed serious health and liability issues.

In 1999, California (which, at the time, consumed nearly 32% of the MTBE used in the United States) petitioned the U.S. Environmental Protection Agency (EPA) for a waiver of the CAAA90 oxygenate requirement.[28] However, California's waiver request was denied by the EPA in mid-2001 since the EPA determined that there was sufficient ethanol production available to replace MTBE.

By 2003, legislation that would phase out or restrict the use of MTBE in gasoline had been passed in 16 states, including California and New York (with a combined 40% national MTBE market share).[29] Between October 1, 2003, and January 1, 2004, over 43% of MTBE consumption in the United States was banned. According to the EIA, the state MTBE ban would require an additional demand for ethanol of 2.73 billion gallons in 2004.

With the legislative boosts and the MTBE phase-out, investments in the biofuels sector began to show results. The number of plants producing ethanol grew from 50 on January 1, 1999, to 81 by January 1, 2005. Concomitantly, U.S. ethanol production began to accelerate, rising to 3.9 billion gallons by 2005 and using over 14% of the nation's corn crop (**Table 1**), up from 1.8 bgals and 7% of the corn crop in 2001.

Table 1. U.S. Corn-Use Share of Annual Production by Major Activity, 1980 to 2012

Period	Ethanol	Food	Exports	Feed
1980-1984	2%	11%	30%	64%
1985-1989	4%	14%	26%	46%
1990-1994	5%	14%	21%	58%
1995-1999	5%	14%	21%	55%
2000-2004	10%	14%	18%	60%
2005-2009	25%	11%	18%	55%
2010-2012	41%	12%	12%	37%

Source: Period averages are calculated by CRS from the USDA, PSD database, March 8, 2013.

Note: Values may sum to greater than 100% because some usage may derive from carryover stocks. The table data for the "Feed" and "Export" categories have not been adjusted to include distillers dried grains and solubles (DDGS)—a protein-rich animal feed that is a by-product of corn-based ethanol production.

The Ethanol Industry's Perfect Storm in 2005

On the heels of the large MTBE phase-out that occurred in 2004 and the surge in ethanol demand, two major events coincided in 2005 to produce extremely favorable economic conditions in the U.S. ethanol sector that persisted through most of 2006. These events included the following.

- The Energy Policy Act of 2005 (EPACT; P.L. 109-58) was signed into law on August 8, 2005. EPACT contained several provisions related to agriculture-based renewable energy production, including biofuels research and funding, expansions of existing biofuels tax credits and creation of new credits, and the creation of the first-ever national minimum-usage mandate, the Renewable Fuels Standard (RFS1; Section 1501), which required that 4 billion gallons (bgals) of ethanol be used domestically in 2006, increasing to 7.5 bgals by 2012.
- In August and September 2005, Hurricanes Katrina and Rita struck the Gulf Coast region causing severe damage to local petroleum importing and refining infrastructure, putting them off-line for several months, and driving gasoline prices sharply higher. Meanwhile, corn prices remained relatively low at about $2 per bushel, creating a period of extreme profitability for the ethanol sector.

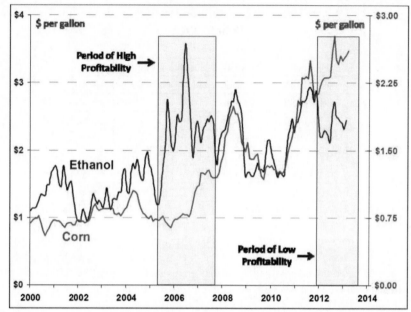

Source: Corn price data are monthly average farm prices, National Agricultural
   Statistics Service (NASS), USDA; ethanol price is the rack price, f.o.b., Nebraska
   Ethanol Board, Nebraska Energy Office, Lincoln, NE.
Note: Corn prices ($ per bushel) have been converted to $ per gallon by CRS—i.e., the
   price of corn used per gallon of ethanol—by dividing the per bushel price by 2.75
   (an estimate of gallons of ethanol per bushel of corn).

Figure 3. Comparison of Monthly Prices: Ethanol versus Corn.

The combination of high ethanol prices and relatively low corn prices that
began in late 2005 and persisted through 2006 and into 2007 created a period
of "unique" profitability for the U.S. ethanol industry (**Figure 3**). At that time,
a 40 million gallon nameplate ethanol plant costing approximately $60 million
could recover its entire capital investment in less than a year of normal
operations.[30] In addition, the establishment of the first RFS—by guaranteeing a
market for new ethanol production—removed much of the investment risk
from the sector.

As a result of this "perfect storm" of policy and market events, investment
money flowed into the construction of new ethanol plants, and U.S. ethanol
production capacity (either in existence or under construction) more than
doubled in just four years, rising from an estimated 4.4 bgals produced in 81
plants in January 2005 to 10.6 bgals produced in 170 plants by January 2009.
The ethanol expansion was almost entirely in dry-mill corn processing plants.

As a result, corn's role as the primary feedstock used in ethanol production in the United States continued to grow. In 2006, corn use for ethanol nearly matched U.S. corn exports at about 2.1 billion bushels. In 2007, U.S. corn exports hit a record 2.4 billion bushels; however, by then corn-for-ethanol use had jumped to over 3 billion bushels. For the first time in U.S. history, the bushels of corn used for ethanol production would be greater than the bushels of corn exported (**Table 1** and **Figure 4**).

EISA Greatly Expands Mandate, Shifts Focus to Cellulosic Biofuels
In light of the rapid expansion of the U.S. biofuels industry, the RFS1 mandate was outgrown in 2006—the same year it was first implemented (**Figure 2**). On December 19, 2007, Congress dramatically raised the "bar" by passing the Energy Independence and Security Act of 2007 (EISA, P.L. 110-140).[31] EISA superseded and greatly expanded EPACT's biofuels mandate relative to historical production (**Figure 5**).

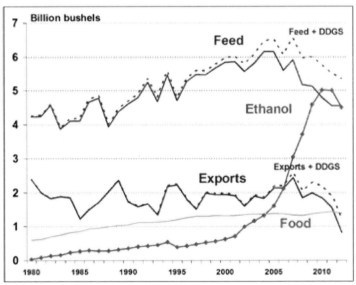

Source: USDA, Production, Supply, and Distribution (PSD) database, March 8, 2013.
Notes: Feed includes a residual category to balance USDA supply and demand estimates. The corn-to-ethanol production process generates a co-product, DDGS, which is a protein-rich animal feed. Both "Feed" and "Export" categories have been adjusted to include DDGS, as shown by the dotted lines.

Figure 4. Annual U.S. Corn Use by Major Activity, 1980 to 2012.

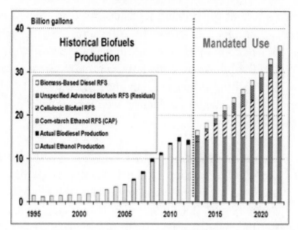

Sources: Actual ethanol production data for 1995-2012 is from Renewable Fuels
    Association; data for RFS2 mandates is from EISA (P.L. 110-140). Data includes
    proposed revision to RFS2 cellulosic mandate for 2013.

Figure 5. Renewable Fuels Standard (RFS2) vs. U.S. Ethanol Production Since 1995.

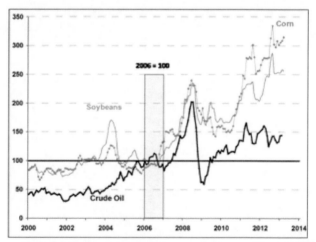

Sources: Corn and soybean prices are monthly average farm prices (MAFPs), National
    Agricultural Statistics Service (NASS), USDA; crude oil is the spot price, f.o.b.,
    for West Texas Intermediate, Cushing, OK, EIA, DOE.
Notes: To facilitate comparison of relative price movements, the monthly prices have
    been converted by CRS to an index where the 12-month average for calendar
    2006 has been set to 100.

Figure 6. Monthly Price Indexes for Corn, Soybeans, and Crude Oil, 2000 to 2013
(nominal monthly prices are indexed such that 2006 = 100).

The expanded RFS (referred to as RFS2) required the use of 9 bgals of biofuels in 2008 and expanded the mandate to 36 bgals annually in 2022. The new mandate had some provisos, foremost of which was that only 15 bgals of annual RFS-qualifying biofuels could be ethanol from corn starch. As a result, all increases in the RFS mandate from 2016 onward must be met by advanced biofuels (i.e., non-corn-starch biofuels) and no less than 16 bgals must be derived from cellulosic feedstock in 2022. In addition, the new mandate established by EISA carved out specific volume requirements for biomass-based diesel fuels.

Meanwhile, prices for many agricultural commodities—including nearly all major U.S. program crops—started a steady upward trend in late 2006. Then, in early 2007, the upward trend for commodity prices turned into a steep rise. By mid-2008 market prices for several agricultural commodities had reached record or near-record levels (Figure 6).[32] In particular, both corn and crude oil hit record high prices in both spot and futures markets, thus symbolizing the growing linkage between U.S. field crops and energy markets.[33]

The upward rise in the price of corn in 2007 and early 2008 sucked the profits out of the U.S. biofuels sector and put the brakes on new investment (**Figure 3**). It also fueled a "food-versus- fuel" debate about the potential for continued expansion in corn use for ethanol to have unintended consequences in other agricultural and environmental markets. While most economists and market analysts agreed that the dramatic price rise of 2008 was due to factors other than biofuels policy, they also are nearly universally agreed that the strong, steady growth in ethanol demand for corn has had an important and sustained upward price effect, not just on the price of corn, but in other agricultural markets including food, feed, fuel, and land.

By mid-2008, the commodity price rise had completely reversed itself and turned into a near free- fall, coinciding with the global financial crisis that broke in late 2008.[34] The extreme price volatility created many difficulties throughout the marketing chain for agricultural buyers and sellers. The experience of $7.00-per-bushel corn, albeit temporary, shattered the idea that biofuels were a panacea for solving the nation's energy security problems and left concerns about the potential for unintended consequences from future biofuels expansion.

2008 Farm Bill Reinforces Focus on Cellulosic Biofuels

The 2008 farm bill (Food, Conservation, and Energy Act of 2008; P.L. 110-246) extended and expanded many existing biofuels programs.[35] In particular, Title XV ("Trade and Tax Provisions") extended the biofuels tax incentives and the tariff on ethanol imports, although the tax credit for corn-starch ethanol was reduced to $0.45 per gallon. But in the wake of the commodity market price run-up of early 2008, the new farm bill also re-emphasized EISA's policy shift towards research and development of advanced and cellulosic bioenergy in an effort to avoid many of the unintended consequences of relying too heavily on major field crops as the principal biomass feedstock. In addition, it established a new tax credit of $1.01 per gallon for cellulosic biofuel.

Like the 2002 farm bill, it contained a distinct energy title (Title IX) that covers a wide range of energy and agricultural topics with extensive attention to biofuels, including corn starch-based ethanol, cellulosic ethanol, and biodiesel. Energy grants and loans are provided through initiatives such as the Bioenergy Program for Advanced Biofuels to promote the development of cellulosic biorefinery capacity. The Repowering Assistance Program supports increasing efficiencies in existing refineries. Programs such as the Rural Energy for America Program (REAP) assist rural communities and businesses in becoming more energy-efficient and self-sufficient, with an emphasis on small operations. Cellulosic feedstocks—for example, switchgrass and woody biomass—are given high priority both in research and funding. The Biomass Crop Assistance Program (BCAP), the Biorefinery Assistance Program, and the Forest Biomass for Energy Program provide support to develop alternative feedstock resources and the infrastructure to support the production, harvest, storage, and processing of cellulosic biomass feedstocks.

Title VII, the research title of the 2008 farm bill, contains numerous renewable-energy-related provisions that promote research, development, and demonstration of biomass-based renewable energy and biofuels. One of the major policy issues debated prior to the passage of the 2008 farm bill was the impact of the rapid, ethanol-driven expansion of U.S. corn production. This issue was made salient by the dramatic surge in commodity prices experienced in 2007 and early 2008. In partial consideration, the enacted bill requires reports on the economic impacts of ethanol production, reflecting concerns that the increasing share of corn production being used for ethanol contributed to high commodity prices and food price inflation.

However, funding authority for Title IX bioenergy programs was fairly limited—about $1 billion in mandatory funding and only slightly more than $100 million in discretionary funding was actually available during the life of the 2008 farm bill (FY2008-FY2012). In addition, all of the major Title IX bioenergy programs expired at the end of FY2012 and lacked baseline funding going forward. The 2008 farm bill (including Title IX) was extended through FY2013 by the American Taxpayer Relief Act (ATRA; P.L. 112-240).[36] However, all major bioenergy provisions of Title IX—with the exception of the Feedstock Flexibility Program for Bioenergy Producers— have no new mandatory funding in FY2013 under the ATRA farm bill extension.

Questions Emerge Concerning Rapid Biofuels Expansion

By 2009, more than half of all U.S. gasoline contained some ethanol (mostly blended at the 10% level or lower). However, national gasoline transportation fuel consumption peaked in 2007 at about 142.5 bgals and has been steadily declining—driven by a weak economy and improving passenger vehicle fuel economy. In 2010 U.S. ethanol consumption reached an estimated 12.9 billion gallons (bgals), which was blended into roughly 138 bgals of gasoline—this represents about 9.3 % of annual gasoline transportation demand on a volume basis.[37]

Meanwhile, robust economic growth in major global markets in 2010 and early 2011 (including China, India, Brazil, and other parts of Asia and the Middle East) reinvigorated international consumer demand and, when coupled with a weak U.S. dollar and events that occurred in international feed grain markets—drought in Russia, Kazakhstan, and the Ukraine in 2010, plus strong Chinese demand for corn and feedstuffs—contributed to record U.S. agricultural export values in 2010 and 2011 and helped to push commodity prices, especially corn, upward again.[38]

By 2010, U.S. ethanol production consumed 40% of the U.S. corn crop and surpassed corn-for- feed use for the first time in history (**Figure 4**). Combined strong demand from export markets and ethanol contributed to near historic low ending stock projections (relative to expected demand) for U.S. corn and soybean for 2010 and 2011.[39] These market conditions helped to spur another surge in agricultural commodity prices starting in mid-2010 (**Figure 6**), thus spreading the effects of rapidly expanding ethanol production and corn demand across several other sectors of the U.S. economy as well.

In addition to expanding domestic production of biofuels, there has been some interest in expanding imports of sugar-based ethanol—usually produced from sugar cane in Brazil—to help satisfy the RFS for advanced biofuels.[40] U.S. sugar-ethanol imports peaked at 660 million gallons in 2006 (including 434 million from Brazil). Market factors in 2010-2012—U.S. ethanol production approaching the "blend wall", high international sugar prices, lower-than-expected sugarcane output in Brazil, and a weak U.S. dollar—

resulted in the United States becoming a net exporter of ethanol during those years (**Figure 7**).[41]

Severe Drought Across Much of Corn Belt Slows Ethanol Industry

In early 2012, high market prices and nearly ideal springtime planting conditions across much of the United States led to substantial and extensive early corn planting. On June 12, 2012, USDA projected U.S. corn plantings of 95.9 million acres—the most since 1937. Normal weather patterns were expected to produce a record 2012 corn harvest of 14.8 billion bushels, which in turn would lead to a build-up in U.S. corn ending stocks in 2013 of nearly 2 billion bushels (up 111% year-to-year), and a 2012/2013 season-average corn price of $4.60/bushel (down 25%).[42] A record harvest and return to low corn prices were eagerly anticipated by both the ethanol and livestock industries.

However, in mid-June, an extensive swath of the Central and Southern Plains and much of the Corn Belt were hit by a combination of extreme heat and dryness that produced what was referred to as a "flash drought." By August 2012—just two months after its optimistic forecast of May— USDA had completely reversed its outlook from one of abundance to one of shortage. USDA lowered its forecast for U.S. corn production to 10.8 billion bushels (a 27% drop of 4 billion bushels from its May forecast), corn price projections were raised sharply to $8.20 per bushel (up 78%), and stocks of feed grains and soybeans were forecast to approach historic low levels relative to demand by the end of 2012/2013 crop year (i.e., at the end of summer 2013).[43]

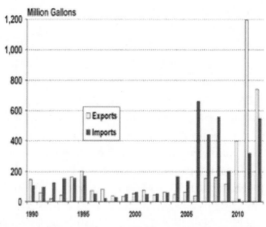

Source: U.S. Department of Commerce, U.S. Census Bureau, Foreign Trade Statistics.

Figure 7. Annual U.S. Ethanol Exports and Imports Since 1990.

Market prices for ethanol were not able to keep up with escalating production costs (primarily for corn) and negative production margins resulted in the idling of several ethanol facilities (Figure 3). As a result, U.S. ethanol production in 2012 declined to 13.3 billion gallons—the first decline in production since 1996, when then-record corn prices temporarily set back ethanol production. The outlook for low corn supplies until the 2013 corn harvest in the September-November period is expected to dampen ethanol production in 2013 as well, possibly reducing it below the 2012 level.[44]

RIN Prices Rise Sharply in Early 2013

Despite waning ethanol production, RFS mandates for biofuel use continued to grow in 2013 to 16.55 bgals of total biofuels, including 2.75 bgals advanced biofuels and a residual 13.8 bgals for corn ethanol. In contrast, national transportation consumption of gasoline-type fuels, which had hit its peak in 2007 at about 142.5 bgals, was projected at slightly under 131 bgals in 2013, with an implied ethanol blend wall of about 13 bgals.[45]

The price for renewable identification numbers (RINs)[46] for basic renewable ethanol (D6)—as reported from thinly traded markets[47]—soared from under $0.05 per gallon during most of 2012 to over $1.00 per gallon in early March 2013.[48] As a result, the RIN values for a fuel blender blending 1 million gallons of E10 (using 100,000 gallons of ethanol) in 2012 might have been $5,000 based on an average ethanol RIN price of about $0.05. The hypothetical value implied for that same volume at $1 per RIN would be $100,000.

The rapid RIN price increase is linked to the impending collision of the RFS mandates and the ethanol blend wall, which, without rapid expansion of the E15 or E85 markets, will likely require the use of accumulated RIN stocks for mandate compliance in 2013 and 2014.

Uncertainties Cloud Biofuels Future

In addition to the ethanol blend wall, the expanded RFS2 is likely to play a dominant role in the development of the U.S. biofuels sector, but with considerable uncertainty regarding spillover effects in other markets and on other important policy goals.[49] The rapid expansion of U.S. corn ethanol production and the concomitant dramatic rise in corn use for ethanol—USDA estimates that over 40% of both the 2011 and 2012 U.S. corn crops was used for ethanol production—has provoked questions about its long-run sustainability and the possibility of unintended consequences in other markets as well as for the environment.[50] Policymakers and the U.S. biofuels industry also are confronted by questions regarding the ability to meet the expanding RFS mandate for biofuels from non-corn sources such as cellulosic biomass materials, whose production capacity has been slow to develop,[51] or biomass-based diesel, which remains expensive to produce owing to the relatively high prices of its feedstocks.

It is widely believed that the ultimate success of the U.S. biofuels sector will depend on its ability to shift away from traditional row crops such as corn or soybeans for processing feedstock, and toward other, cheaper forms of biomass—such as prairie grass or algae—that do not compete with traditional food crops for land and other resources. Recent federal biofuels policies have attempted to assist this shift by focusing on the development of a cellulosic biofuels industry.[52] However, the speed of cellulosic biofuels development remains a major uncertainty, since new technologies must first emerge and be implemented on a commercial scale. The uncertainty surrounding the development of such new technologies and their commercial adaptation has been a major impediment to the flow of much needed private-sector investment funds into the cellulosic biofuels sector.

Ethanol Production Capacity Centered in Corn Belt

As of April 8, 2013, U.S. ethanol production was underway or planned in 210 plants located in 28 states based primarily around the central and western Corn Belt, where corn supplies are most plentiful (**Table 2** and **Figure 8**). Existing U.S. ethanol plant capacity was estimated at 14.763 billion gallons per year (BGPY), with another 0.158 BGPY of capacity under construction (either as new plants or expansion of existing plants). Thus, total annual U.S. ethanol production capacity in existence or under construction was about 14.9 BGPY, well in excess of the 13.8 bgals RFS2 corn-starch ethanol residual quota for 2013 (**Figure 2**).

Iowa is by far the leading ethanol-producing state, with a 30% share of total U.S. output. The top six Corn Belt states of Iowa, Nebraska, Illinois, Minnesota, South Dakota, and Indiana account for nearly 75% of national production (**Table 2**). On a national level, actual operating capacity of 13.2 BGPY represents about 89% of nameplate capacity. This is because several states, including Nebraska, Minnesota, Indiana, Kansas, Ohio, and the "other" category of states, are operating substantially below their nameplate capacity, suggesting that poor industry profitability has been widespread across the country, primarily due to high feedstock cost and limited availability.

EVOLUTION OF THE U.S. BIODIESEL SECTOR

Biodiesel can be produced from any animal fat or vegetable oil (such as soybean oil or recycled cooking oil). Historically, most U.S. biodiesel was made from soybean oil. As a result, U.S. soybean producers and the American Soybean Association (ASA) are strong advocates for greater government support for biodiesel production. However, with the rise in soybean prices since 2007 (**Figure 6**), biodiesel producers have aggressively shifted to cheaper vegetable oils and animal fats (especially poultry fat), such that by 2011 nearly 44% of U.S. biodiesel production was estimated to be based on sources other than soybean oil.[53] In recent years, many ethanol production facilities have added technology to remove corn oil from distillers grains and solubles, thus generating an additional income stream to help offset depressed profit margins.[54] The corn oil produced by this "end-stream" technology is typically not suitable for the food industry. Instead, the main uses of this added corn oil has been as an energy supplement in livestock and poultry rations, and for biodiesel production.

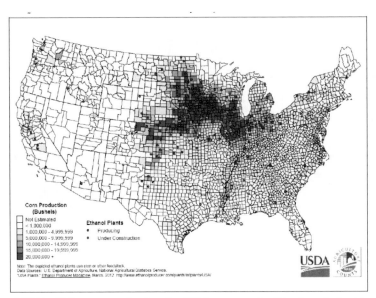

Source: USDA; U.S. corn production for 2011 compared with ethanol plant locations as of March 8; 2012; available at http://www.nass.usda.gov/ Charts_and_Maps /Ethanol_Plants/U._S._Ethanol_Plants/index.asp.

Figure 8. U.S. Ethanol Production Capacity Is Centered on the Corn Belt.

Table 2. U.S. Ethanol Output and Production Capacity by State

| Rank | State | # of Plants | Operating Production | | | Current Nameplate Capacity (MGPY) | Under Contr. or Expansion (MGPY) |
			MGPY	% of output	Cumulative% output		
1	Iowa	41	3,903	30%	30%	3,908	—
2	Nebraska	27	1,509	11%	41%	1,822	—
3	Illinois	14	1,413	11%	52%	1,454	—
4	Minnesota	22	1,110	8%	60%	1,225	—
5	S. Dakota	15	1,016	8%	68%	1,016	—
6	Indiana	14	947	7%	75%	1,136	—
7	Wisconsin	9	504	4%	79%	504	5
8	Ohio	7	478	4%	82%	538	—
9	Kansas	13	386	3%	85%	507	45
10	N. Dakota	4	360	3%	88%	360	—
11	Michigan	5	268	2%	90%	268	—
12	Tennessee	2	225	2%	92%	225	—
13	Missouri	6	210	2%	93%	271	—
14	Texas	4	205	2%	95%	355	—
15	New York	2	164	1%	96%	164	—
	Others (13)	25	506	4%	100%	1,010	108
U.S. Total		**210**	**13,203**	**100%**		**14,763**	**158**

Source: Renewable Fuels Association as of April 8, 2013; state-level aggregations are by CRS and include several approximations of current plant operating levels.
Note: Output and production capacity data are in million gallons per year (MPGY).

According to the National Biodiesel Board (NBB), biodiesel is nontoxic, biodegradable, and essentially free of sulfur and aromatics. In addition, it works in any diesel engine with few or no modifications and offers similar fuel economy, horsepower, and torque, but with superior lubricity and important emission improvements over petroleum diesel.[55]

To date, biodiesel is used almost uniquely as a substitute for petroleum diesel transport fuel. Biodiesel delivers slightly less energy than petroleum diesel (about 92%); however, U.S. biodiesel consumption remains small relative to national diesel consumption levels. In 2012 (**Figure 1**), U.S. biodiesel consumption represented about 1.5% (in diesel-equivalent units) of national diesel transportation fuel use of about 46.8 billion gallons.[56]

Biodiesel is compatible with existing petroleum-based diesel vehicles and infrastructure (fuel tanks, retail pumps, delivery infrastructure etc.) such that biodiesel does not face a blend wall similar to ethanol. As a result, the potential blending pool for biodiesel is significantly larger than just the transportation diesel fuel market. Because biodiesel and diesel fuel are so similar, biodiesel can also be used for the same non-transportation activities— the two largest of which are home heating and power generation. In 2012, 53.2 billion gallons of diesel fuel were used for heating and power generation by residential, commercial, and industry, and by railroad and vessel traffic, bringing total U.S. diesel fuel use to nearly 106.7 billion gallons (including 46.8 billion gallons of transportation fuel use and 6.8 billion gallons of residual fuel oil).

Fuel blenders and consumers are very sensitive to price differences between biodiesel and petroleum-based diesel. The price relationship between vegetable oils and petroleum diesel is the key determinant of profitability in the biodiesel industry—about 7.5 pounds of vegetable oil are used in each gallon of biodiesel. Since late 2010, soybean oil prices have averaged over $0.50/lb. such that the vegetable oil feedstock component of biodiesel has cost over $3.75/gal. Additional processing and marketing costs likely push wholesale biodiesel prices into the $4.50/gal. to $5.00/gal. range compared with petroleum diesel wholesale prices of $3.05/gallon during that period. As a result, the biodiesel industry has depended on federal support—especially the production tax credit and the RFS for biomass-based diesel—for its economic survival.

Federal Programs Help Kick-Start U.S. Biodiesel Production

The U.S. biodiesel industry did not emerge until the late 1990s. In 1999, U.S. biodiesel production was still less than 1 million gallons. Bioenergy Program payments provided an initial impetus for biodiesel plant investments from 2001 through 2006. The American Jobs Creation Act of 2004 (P.L. 108-357) created the first ever federal biodiesel tax incentive—a federal excise tax and income tax credit of $1.00 for every gallon of agri-biodiesel (i.e., virgin vegetable oil and animal fat) that was used in blending with petroleum diesel; and a $0.50 credit for every gallon of non-agri-biodiesel (i.e., recycled oils such as yellow grease). The distinction between biodiesel from virgin and recycled oils was eventually removed (P.L. 110-343; October 3, 2008), and all biodiesel qualified for the credit of $1.00 per gal.

Starting in late 2005 through 2006, the U.S. biodiesel industry received a major economic boost from the same series of market and policy developments described for ethanol—i.e., high petroleum prices and low agricultural commodity prices.[57] Soybean oil prices were still relatively low priced during the 2000 through 2006 period, when they averaged $0.21/lb. (this compares with an average of nearly $0.44/lb. since 2007). The Energy Policy Act of 2005 extended the biodiesel tax credit and established a Small Agri-Biodiesel Producer Credit of $0.10 per gallon on the first 15 million gallons of biodiesel produced from plants with production capacity below 60 million gallons per year.

Biomass-based diesel (BBD) was not part of the initial biofuels RFS1 mandate under the Energy Policy Act of 2005, but was included as a distinct category in the RFS2 created under EISA of 2007. While most of this mandate is expected to be met using biodiesel, other fuels, including renewable diesel,[58] algae-based diesel, or cellulosic diesel, would also qualify.

Starting in mid-2007, the U.S. biodiesel industry suffered from unfavorable market conditions as prices for vegetable oil rose relative to diesel fuel (the monthly average wholesale price for soybean oil in Decatur, Illinois, hit $0.62/lb. in June 2008, implying a per-gallon cost of $4.65 for biodiesel). Most biodiesel plants continued to operate into 2008 in hopes of either higher diesel prices or lower vegetable oil prices, and the industry produced then-record output of an estimated 678 million gallons (**Figure 9**).[59] However, the financial crisis of late 2008 and the ensuing economic recession weakened demand for transportation fuel, and petroleum prices (including diesel fuel) fell sharply in the second half of 2008.

Starting in 2007 and 2008, U.S. biodiesel producers (relying heavily on the $1/gallon production tax credit) were able to take advantage of a favorable price relationship vis-à-vis the European Union (EU)—which also had domestic policies that encouraged biodiesel consumption—and profitably exported substantial volumes of U.S.-produced biodiesel to the EU. As a result, U.S. biodiesel exports soared to a record 677 million gallons in 2008. However, in March 2009, the EU imposed anti-dumping and countervailing duty tariffs on imports of U.S. biodiesel that effectively shut down U.S. biodiesel exports to the EU and cut in half a major supply outlet for U.S. biodiesel producers (**Figure 10**).[61]

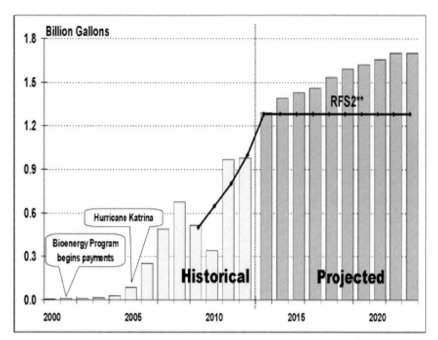

Source: Data for 1999-2012, Energy Information Agency, DOE. Projections for 2013-2022 are from FAPRI, *FAPRI-MU Biofuel Baseline*, FAPRI-MU Report #02-13, March 2013. FAPRI projections assume that market conditions, driven in part by the RFS for advanced biofuel, result in BBD consumption above the RFS for BBD.

Notes: RFS2** shown in the chart represents the RFS for BBD. Although the RFS2 mandate for biodiesel was to begin in 2009, implementation rules were not available until February 2010. As a result, the RFS2 mandate for 2009 of 500 million gallons was combined with the 2010 mandate of 650 million gallons for a one-time mandate of 1.15 billion gallons in 2010. In 2011, the mandate returned to its original trajectory of 800 million gallons, rising to 1 billion gallons in 2012. Starting in 2013, EPA is directed to establish the BBD RFS at no less than 1 billion gallons through a future rulemaking. In its 2013 RFS proposal, EPA proposed a BBD RFS of 1.28 billion gallons.[60] FAPRI assumes that it remains at that level through FY2022.

Figure 9. Annual U.S. Bio-Based Diesel (BBD) Production 1999 to 2022.

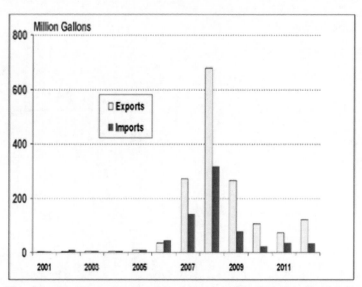

Source: EIA, *Monthly Energy Review*, March 2013, Table 10.4 "Biodiesel Overview."

Figure 10. Annual U.S. Biodiesel Exports and Imports Since 2001.

As a result, the U.S. biodiesel industry experienced several bankruptcies and some loss of capacity during 2009. U.S. biodiesel production in 2009 fell to 516 million gallons, down 24% from 2008.[62] The unfavorable economic conditions for biodiesel production extended into 2010 and were made worse by the expiration of the biodiesel tax credit at the end of 2009. The tax credit was eventually renewed on December 17, 2010 (P.L. 111-312), and made available retroactively to all 2010 biodiesel production; however, the extended delay and poor market conditions contributed to substantially reduced U.S. biodiesel production of 343 million gallons in 2010. During 2010, the U.S. biodiesel industry saw 52 out of 170 operating plants stop operations while many others scaled back on production.[63] The renewal of the tax credit and the expanded RFS2 biodiesel usage mandate of 800 million gallons in 2011 revived the industry and spurred record production of 967 million gallons in 2011 (**Figure 9**).

Once again both the biodiesel tax credit ($1.00/gallon) and the small agri-biodiesel producer credit ($0.10/gallon on the first 15 million gallons) expired at the end of 2011, but were extended through 2013 by P.L. 112-240, which retroactively applied the extension to fuel produced in 2012. In addition to the retroactive tax credit, biodiesel production in 2012 was supported by the RFS2 biodiesel mandate, which grew to 1 billion gallons in 2012. U.S. biodiesel production eclipsed the previous year's record with an output of 969 million gallons in 2012.

Two factors are expected to support biodiesel production at or above 1.28 billion gallons starting in 2013 and going forward: first, the RFS2 biodiesel mandate for 2013 has been proposed at 1.28 billion gallons by EPA; second, the RFS2 for advanced biofuels (for which biodiesel is a qualifying fuel) grows even faster, with 2.75 billion gallons in 2013 rising to 21 billion gallons by 2022. Although cellulosic biofuel was originally envisioned to fill most of the advanced biofuel mandate, slow progress in commercial production to date suggests that biodiesel may be used to meet at least a portion of the advanced biofuel mandate in the future. If this projected outcome were to be realized, it would likely have a profound impact on vegetable oil markets, as biodiesel production would be expected to consume an increasingly larger share of available supplies.[64]

Biodiesel Production Capacity Spreads Nationwide

As mentioned earlier, the primary feedstock for biodiesel includes both vegetable oils and animal fats, both of which are produced over a greater geographic area than corn. As a result, biodiesel plants are more widely dispersed across the United States than are ethanol plants (**Table 3**). As of January 2013, there were 110 companies in the United States with the potential to produce biodiesel commercially that were either in operation or idled, with total annual production capacity (within the oleo-chemical industry) of 2.1 billion gallons per year. Because many of these plants also can produce other products such as cosmetics, estimated total capacity (and capacity for expansion) is far greater than actual biodiesel production.

The unfavorable economic conditions of 2009 and 2010, coupled with the delays in extending the biodiesel tax credit first in 2010 and then again in 2012, and finally the run-up in soybean and product prices in 2011 and 2012, all contributed to a substantial shake-up in the biodiesel industry. Many plants situated in the heart of corn and soybean country dropped out of business, while new plants sprang up in locations near alternate vegetable or animal oil sources. As a result, the U.S. biodiesel industry is more diversified and less centralized than the ethanol industry. Unlike ethanol, where the top six producing states account for 75% of national capacity, the top six biodiesel-producing states achieve only a 58% share, thus demonstrating the more widespread nature of U.S. biodiesel production capacity.

U.S. TRANSPORTATION FUEL INFRASTRUCTURE

A key determinant of the demand for biofuels as a transportation fuel is the size and fuel economy of the U.S. vehicle fleet, and the adequacy of the infrastructure (e.g., pipelines, storage tanks, service pumps) that delivers transportation fuel to consumers at the retail level. According to the Department of Energy (DOE), 73% of U.S. transportation fuel is consumed as gasoline or gasoline blends (**Figure 1**), with the remainder consumed as diesel fuel. Gasoline blends and diesel fuel, for the most part, require different infrastructure for delivery to the retail market. In addition, vehicle motors are designed to operate with either gasoline or diesel, but not both.

U.S. Vehicle Fleet

The U.S. Department of Transportation (DOT) estimated that there were 250.2 million registered passenger vehicles (including trucks, buses, and motorcycles) in the United States in 2011, down slightly from 254.2 million in 2009.[65] Included in the fleet of passenger vehicles are more than 14 million flex-fuel vehicles (FFVs), which are capable of operating on the standard 10% ethanol and 90% gasoline (E10) blends as well as higher ethanol blends up to 85% ethanol and 15% gasoline (E85).[66]

Gasoline-Blend Infrastructure Issues

Because of its physical properties, pure ethanol cannot be used in the same infrastructure used to deliver retail gasoline. Nor can ethanol be used in standard automobile engines at high blend ratios, because ethanol tends to make the engine run at a higher temperature than standard reformulated gasoline. In addition, the presence of ethanol can be corrosive on rubber and plastic parts in the car engine. In contrast, biodiesel is very similar in nature to petroleum diesel and does not have the same infrastructure limitations.

The Blend Wall and Higher-Level Ethanol Blends
Prior to October 2010, the amount of ethanol that could be blended in gasoline for use in standard vehicle motors without modification was limited to 10% by volume (E10), by guidance developed by the EPA under the Clean Air Act, and certification procedures for fuel-dispensing equipment. In

addition, most vehicle warranties did not cover any motor damage resulting from use of ethanol blends above 10%. In the past, only flex-fuel vehicles (FFVs) have been capable of using higher ethanol blends.

As a result, this 10% blend has represented an upper bound (sometimes referred to as the "blend wall") to the amount of ethanol that can be introduced into the gasoline pool.[67] If most or all gasoline in the country contained 10% ethanol, this would allow only for roughly 13 billion gallons, far less than the RFS mandates for 2013 onward.

For ethanol consumption to exceed the so-called blend wall and meet the RFS mandates, increased consumption at higher blending ratios is needed. For example, raising the blending limit from 10% to a higher ratio such as 15% or 20% would immediately expand the "blend wall" to somewhere in the range of 20 billion to 27 billion gallons. The U.S. ethanol industry is a strong proponent of raising the blending ratio.

Table 3. U.S. Biodiesel Production Capacity Partial Estimate as of January 2013

Rank	State	# of Plants	Production Capacity (MGY)	% of Output	Cumulative % output
1	Texas	11	408	20%	20%
2	Iowa	8	250	12%	32%
3	Missouri	8	170	8%	40%
4	Illinois	5	166	8%	48%
5	Washington	4	109	5%	53%
6	Minnesota	4	107	5%	58%
7	Mississippi	3	105	5%	63%
8	Indiana	2	104	5%	68%
9	Pennsylvania	6	90	4%	72%
10	Arkansas	3	85	4%	76%
11	N. Dakota	1	85	4%	80%
12	Kentucky	5	68	3%	84%
13	Ohio	3	67	3%	87%
14	California	9	57	3%	90%
15	Alabama	2	49	2%	92%
	Others (22)	36	168	8%	100%
U.S. Total		**110**	**2,086**	**100%**	

Source: U.S. EIA, "Table 4. Biodiesel Producers and Production Capacity by State, January 2013," *Monthly Biodiesel Production Report*, March 28, 2013.

The blend wall problem is made more acute by substantial revisions in EIA's projections of U.S. transportation fuel consumption rates since the RFS was first passed into law in 2007 (**Figure 11**). At that time, EIA estimated that U.S. transportation consumers were using about 145 billion gallons of gasoline (including ethanol) per year, but that consumption would grow strongly to 176 billion gallons of gasoline by 2022—as a result, RFS mandated biofuels would represent about 19% of annual gasoline consumption. By 2013, EIA had substantially lowered its fuel consumption outlook—partly due to sustained high petroleum prices, the prolonged effects of the 2008 financial crisis on consumer incomes, and significantly higher fuel economy standards on new vehicles. Instead of growth, EIA projects gasoline consumption to fall to about 120 billion gallons by 2022, thus causing the RFS mandate's share of the gasoline transportation fuel market to grow to nearly 20% of annual consumption (in gasoline-equivalent gallons).[68]

EPA Ruling on the Ethanol-to-Gasoline Blending Limit: 10% vs. 15%

On March 6, 2009, Growth Energy (on behalf of 52 U.S. ethanol producers) applied to the EPA for a waiver from the then-current Clean Air Act E10 limit and an increase in the maximum allowable concentration to 15% (E15). After substantial vehicle testing, the EPA issued, first a partial waiver (October 2010) for gasoline that contains up to a 15% ethanol blend (E15) for use in model year 2007 or newer passenger vehicles (including cars, SUVs, and light pickup trucks).[69] Then after further testing, on January 21, 2011, EPA expanded the eligible passenger vehicle pool to include model years 2001 through 2006.[70]

However, EPA also announced that no waiver would be granted for E15 use in model year 2000 and older light-duty motor vehicles, as well as in any motorcycles, heavy duty vehicles, or non- road engines. This later restriction opens up the possibility of "mis-fueling"—that is, using higher ethanol blends in vehicles not appropriate for the EPA 15% blend waiver.[71] According to the Renewable Fuel Association (RFA), the approval of E15 use in model year 2001 and newer passenger vehicles covered 62% of passenger vehicles on U.S. roads at the end of 2010.[72]

These EPA rulings would appear to have expanded the eligible vehicle pool for ethanol blends greater than 10%. However, two factors prevent a blend wall expansion to 15%. First, U.S. automakers have not yet extended vehicle warranties to cover any motor damage resulting from use of ethanol blends above 10%. Second, the fact that a portion of currently active passenger vehicles are not eligible for E15—i.e., model year 2000 or older—both limits ethanol retail delivery opportunities and raises the cost of delivery, thus inhibiting retailer adoption.

Alternate Options to the Blend Wall

Two additional options to resolving this bottleneck exist, but appear to be long-run alternatives. The first is to increase the use of ethanol in flex-fuel vehicles (FFVs) at ethanol-to-gasoline blend ratios as high as E85. However, increased E85 use would involve substantial infrastructure development, particularly in the number of designated storage tanks and E85 retail pumps, as well as a further expansion of the FFV fleet to absorb larger volumes of ethanol.

According to the Renewable Fuels Association (RFA), more than 14 million FFVs were on the roads in 2012, representing over 5% of U.S. passenger vehicles. However, not all FFV owners have access to (or choose to use) E85 retail pumps. As of early 2013, over 3,000 retail stations in the United States offered E85 (2% out of 142,000 stations).[73] Most E85 fueling stations are concentrated in the midwestern states near the current ethanol production heartland (**Figure 12**).

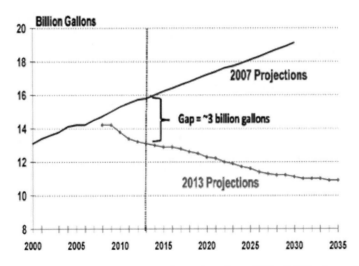

Source: Calculations are by CRS based on data from EIA, DOE, *Annual Energy Review* 2007 and *Annual Energy Review* 2013.

Notes: The blend wall is calculated as a simple 10% share of projections for U.S. gasoline consumption.

Figure 11. Ethanol Blend Wall Projections, 2007 vs. 2013.

In addition, at blend ratios above 10%, ethanol must compete directly with gasoline as a transportation fuel. For ethanol to operate primarily as a gasoline substitute, it must be priced competitively with gasoline on an energy-content or miles-per-gallon basis.

A second alternative is to expand use of processing technologies at the biofuel plant to produce biofuels in a "drop-in" form (e.g., butanol) that can be used by existing petroleum-based distribution and storage infrastructure and the current fleet of U.S. vehicles. However, more infrastructure-friendly biofuels generally require more processing than ethanol and are therefore more expensive to produce.

FEDERAL PROGRAMS THAT SUPPORT BIOFUELS

Federal Biofuels Policies Have Encouraged Rapid Growth ...

Federal biofuels programs have proven critical to the economic success of the U.S. biofuels industry, primarily ethanol and biodiesel, whose output has grown rapidly in recent years. Initially, federal biofuels policies were developed to help kick-start the biofuels industry during its early development, when neither production capacity nor a market for the finished product were widely available. Federal policy played a key role in underwriting the initial investments in biofuels production capacity as well as in helping to close the price gap between biofuels and cheaper petroleum fuels.

During the rapid growth period of 2006-2011, U.S. biofuels production and supporting federal budget outlays grew concomitantly. Federal support for biofuels production peaked in 2011, when an estimated $7.7 billion of direct support—including tax credit expenditures ($7.3 billion) and 2008 farm bill Title IX outlays (approximately $300 million)—was incurred.[74] Federal outlays in 2012 are estimated sharply lower, at about $1.3 billion, due to the expiration of several biofuels tax credits.

... And Conflicting Viewpoints

The trade-offs between benefits to farm and rural economies, as opposed to large federal budget costs and the potential for unintended consequences, have led to emergence of both proponents and critics of the government subsidies and mandates that underwrite biofuels production. Oversight and implementation of federal biofuels policies is spread across several government agencies, but the primary responsibility lies with EPA, USDA, and DOE. As the number, complexity, and budgetary implications of federal biofuels policies have grown, so too has the number of proponents and critics.

Proponents of government support for agriculture-based biofuels production have cited national energy security, reductions in greenhouse gas emissions, and raising domestic demand for U.S.- produced farm products as viable justifications. In many cases, biofuels are more environmentally friendly (in terms of emissions of toxins, volatile organic compounds, and greenhouse gases) than petroleum products. In addition, proponents argue that rural, agriculture-based energy production can enhance rural incomes and expand employment opportunities, while encouraging greater value-added for U.S. agricultural commodities.[75]

In contrast, critics argue that, in the absence of subsidies, current biofuels production strategies can only be economically competitive with existing fossil fuels at much higher petroleum prices, or if significant improvements in existing technologies are made or new technologies are developed.[76] Until such technological breakthroughs are achieved, critics contend that the subsidies distort energy market incentives and divert research funds from the development of other renewable energy sources, such as solar or geothermal, that offer potentially cleaner, more bountiful alternatives. Still others question the rationale behind policies that promote biofuels for energy security. These critics question whether the United States could ever produce sufficient feedstock of starches, sugars, or vegetable oils to permit biofuels production to meaningfully offset petroleum imports.[77] Critics from the petroleum industry argue against the economic costs associated with the imposition of biofuels blending requirements.[78] Finally, some (particularly environmental watchdog groups) argue that the focus on development of alternative energy sources undermines efforts for greater conservation to reduce energy waste.

Many biofuels-related policy debates occur along geographic lines. For example, Midwest corn- and ethanol-producing states are major proponents of federal policy support, whereas many residents of the East and West Coast urban states perceive expensive biofuel usage mandates as being forced upon them while their access to cheaper Brazilian sugar-cane ethanol was, for many years, limited by an import tariff. Another source of biofuels policy conflict has emerged between the major users of corn. Livestock producers have seen their feed costs escalate with the growth in biofuels corn demand and are highly critical of further federal biofuels support.

Source: U.S. DOE, Alternative Fuels and Advanced Vehicles Data Center, November
    2010, available at http://www.afdc.energy.gov/afdc/ethanol/ethanol_locations.
    html.

Figure 12. E85 Refueling Locations by State.

Federal Biofuels Programs Described

Most of the biofuels policies developed and funded by Congress are
subject to oversight and periodic reauthorization.[79] For most of the past three
decades, three types of federal programs have provided the core support for
the U.S. biofuels industry: blending and production tax credits to lower the
cost of biofuels to end users, an import tariff to protect domestic ethanol from
cheaper foreign-produced ethanol, and volume-specific usage mandates to
guarantee a market for biofuels irrespective of their cost. In addition, the
biofuels industry has been supported by several indirect policies in the form of
research grants to stimulate the development of new technologies, and grants,
loans, and loan guarantees to facilitate the development of biofuels feedstocks
as well as market and distribution infrastructure.

Tax Credits

Various tax credits and other incentives have been available for the
production, blending, and/or sale of biofuels and biofuel blends (**Table 4**). Tax
credits vary by the type of fuel and the size of the producer. Because of their
budgetary cost, the tax credits are rarely extended for more than a year or two
at a time. As a result, they routinely require congressional action to be
extended. On December 31, 2011, most biofuels blending and production tax

credits expired, with the exception of the cellulosic biofuels production tax credit, which was set to expire at the end of 2012. The American Tax Payer Relief Act of 2012 (P.L. 112-240) extended both the producer and small producer tax credits for biodiesel, renewable diesel, and cellulosic biofuels through 2013 and retroactively for 2012.

Import Tariff on Foreign-Produced Ethanol

Prior to 2012, most imported ethanol was subject to a most-favored-nation duty set of $0.54 per gallon of ethanol (for fuel use) and a 2.5% ad valorem tariff. The stated goal of the import tariff was to offset the ethanol blending tax credit which was also available for foreign-produced ethanol. However, the fixed $0.54-per-gallon most favored-nation duty (identified by 9901.00.50 and 9901.00.52 of the Harmonized Tariff System (HTS)) expired on December 31, 2011. The 2.5% ad valorem tariff (2207.10.60 of the HTS) does not expire but is permanent until or unless the HTS code itself is changed. In most years the tariff was a significant barrier to direct imports of Brazilian sugarcane ethanol. However, some Brazilian ethanol could be brought into the United States duty-free if it was dehydrated (reprocessed) in Caribbean Basin Initiative (CBI) countries.[80] Up to 7% of the U.S. ethanol market could be supplied duty-free in this fashion; historically, however, ethanol dehydrated in CBI countries has only represented about 2% of the total U.S. market.

The Renewable Fuel Standard (RFS)[81]

As described earlier, the RFS requires the blending of renewable fuels (including ethanol and biodiesel) in U.S. transportation fuel.[82] The RFS is administered by EPA. Under the RFS, fuel blenders are required to blend an increasing amount of renewable fuel in the national transportation fuel supply. This requirement increases annually from 9 billion gallons (bgals) in 2008 to 36 bgals in 2022, of which only 15 bgals can be ethanol from corn starch. The remaining 21 bgals are to be so-called "advanced biofuels"—fuels produced from non-corn-starch feedstocks—of which 16 bgals are to be from cellulosic biofuels, 1 bgals from biomass-based diesel, and 4 bgals from other biofuels (most likely imported sugar-cane ethanol from Brazil). Qualifying biofuels must meet explicit criteria on lifecycle greenhouse gas (GHG) emissions[83] and feedstock production pathways (including restrictions on the land on which feedstocks are produced, feedstock production methods, and the biofuels plant processing technology).

Table 4. Federal Tax Credits Available for Qualifying Biofuels

Biofuel	Tax Credit: $/gallon	Details	Expiration Date
Volumetric Ethanol Excise Tax Credit (VEETC)	$0.45	Available in unlimited amount to all qualifying biofuels.	Expired Dec. 31, 2011
Small Ethanol Producer Credit	$0.10	Available on the first 15 million gallons (mgal) of any producer with production capacity below 60 mgal.	Expired Dec. 31, 2011
Biodiesel Tax Credit	$1.00	Available in unlimited amount to all qualifying biodiesel.	Dec. 31, 2013[a]
Small Agri-Biodiesel Producer Credit	$0.10	Available on the first 15 mgal of any producer with production capacity below 60 mgal.	Dec. 31, 2013[a]
Renewable Diesel Tax Credit	$1.00	Available in unlimited amount to all qualifying biodiesel.	Dec. 31, 2013[a]
Credit for Production of Cellulosic and Algae-Based Biofuel[b]	$1.01	Available in unlimited amount to all qualifying biofuels.	Dec. 31, 2013[a]

Source: CRS Report R42566, *Alternative Fuel and Advanced Vehicle Technology Incentives: A Summary of Federal Programs.*

a. The tax credit originally expired at the end of 2009 and was not extended until the passage of P.L. 111-312, which retroactively applied the extension to fuel produced in 2010. The tax credit also expired at the end of 2011 and was extended through 2013 by P.L. 112-240, which retroactively applied the extension to fuel produced in 2012.

b. P.L. 112-240, amended the credit to included non-cellulosic fuel produced from algae feedstocks.

Other Indirect Federal Policies

Several additional biofuels programs have been created to provide various grants, loans, and loan guarantees in support of research and development of related technology, as well as support for biofuels infrastructure development. Many of these programs reside in the energy title (Title IX) of the 2008 farm bill (P.L. 110-246).[84] Federal programs also require federal agencies to give preference to bio-based products in purchasing fuels and other supplies. Cellulosic plant investment is further facilitated by a special depreciation allowance created under the Tax Relief and Health Care Act of 2006 (P.L. 109-432).[85] Also, several states have their own incentives, regulations, and programs in support of renewable fuel research, production, and use that supplement or exceed federal incentives.[86]

In addition to direct and indirect biofuels policies, the U.S. biofuels industry benefits from U.S. farm programs in the form of price and income support programs (i.e., marketing loan benefits and the counter-cyclical payment program) and risk-reducing farm programs (e.g., Acreage Crop Revenue Election (ACRE), Supplemental Revenue Assistance Payments (SURE), federal crop insurance, and disaster assistance), which encourage greater production and lower prices than would occur in the absence of federal programs in a free-market equilibrium.[87] As a result, agricultural feedstocks are both lower-priced and more abundant than without federal farm programs. This helps lower production costs for the U.S. biofuels sector, and makes U.S. biofuels more competitive with foreign-produced biofuels.

CURRENT BIOFUELS POLICY ISSUES

Most of the federal biofuels tax credit provisions, as well as the import tariff on foreign-produced ethanol, have short legislative lives and require frequent extension. The primary energy-related issue for the next farm bill is the expiration of program authority at the end of FY2013 and the current lack of mandatory funding going forward for all major energy-related provisions of Title IX.[88] In addition, the appearance of substantial redundancy across renewable energy programs at USDA and DOE, the slow development of the U.S. cellulosic biofuels sector, and concerns about the emerging spillover effects of increasing corn use for ethanol production are issues that are likely to emerge during the next farm bill debate.

Pending Congressional Actions

2008 Farm Bill Expiration
Many provisions of the 2008 farm bill expired at the end of FY2012, but were extended through FY2013 by the American Taxpayer Relief Act (ATRA; P.L. 112-240).[89] Authority for Title IX biofuels policy provisions contained in the 2008 farm bill (P.L. 110-246) also were extended through FY2013, and are expected to be reviewed as part of the next farm bill debate.[90] However, all

major bioenergy provisions of Title IX—with the exception of the Feedstock Flexibility Program for Bioenergy Producers—have no new mandatory funding in FY2013 under the ATRA farm bill extension. Although most of the bioenergy programs are reauthorized for FY2013, their mandatory funding expired at the end of FY2012. If policymakers want to continue these programs under either the 2008 farm bill extension or in the next farm bill, they will need to pay for the program with offsets.

The 2008 farm bill authorized $1.1 billion in mandatory funding for energy programs, including $320 million for the Biorefinery Assistance Program, $300 million for the Bioenergy Program for Advanced Biofuels, and $255 million for the Rural Energy for America Program (REAP). The Biomass Crop Assistance Program (BCAP) was authorized to receive such sums as necessary (i.e., funding is open-ended and depends on program participation), although Congress eventually put limits on mandatory funding of $552 million in FY2010, $112 million in FY2011, and $17 million in FY2012. None of the major farm-bill energy programs have baseline funding after FY2012. As a result, the federal budget rules require new revenues or offsetting cuts in order to extend them beyond FY2012.

Cellulosic Biofuels Tax Credit

While most ethanol tax credits and the import duty on foreign fuel ethanol expired on December 31, 2011, the cellulosic biofuel tax credit and the various biodiesel tax credits do not expire until December 31, 2013. Both the cellulosic biofuels and biodiesel industries can be expected to lobby actively for extension of their tax credits. However, a tight federal budget combined with lack of progress in developing commercial production of cellulosic biofuels are likely to work against an extension. At $1.00 per gallon, the biodiesel tax credit is projected to cost at least $1.28 billion in tax expenditures in 2012, whereas the cellulosic biofuels tax credit is projected to cost about $14 million.

Cellulosic Biofuels Feedstock Program: BCAP

Investors have been slow to invest in what so far is a commercially unproven technology—the conversion of cellulosic biomass to biofuels. Development of the cellulosic biofuels industry hinges on the effective use of new feedstocks. The Biomass Crop Assistance Program (BCAP) was created under the 2008 farm bill to facilitate the development of those new feedstocks and kick-start the cellulosic biofuels industry.[91] BCAP (via USDA's CCC) provides financial assistance in two forms: (1) to support the establishment and production of eligible crops for conversion to bioenergy in selected areas, and (2) to assist agricultural and forest land owners and operators with collection, harvest, storage, and transportation (CHST) of eligible material for use in a biomass conversion facility.

While BCAP is in the early stages of implementation, concerns regarding eligibility, funding, and sustainability continue to be discussed. These issues could shape future congressional action on the program in the context of budgetary measures and possible reauthorization in the next farm bill. In particular, BCAP does not include "baseline" budget spending beyond FY2012. Based on current budgetary requirements, the authorizing committees could potentially need to secure offset funding if BCAP were to be reauthorized in the next farm bill. This could prove difficult given tight budgetary constraints and the more recent and higher projections of the program's cost compared to its initial cost estimates.

Proposed Biofuels-Related Bills in the 113th Congress

The current federal biofuels programs continue to inspire strong sentiments from both advocates and detractors. Several Members of Congress have introduced bills that would either strengthen or reduce (and even eliminate) certain features of current programs.

Pending EPA Actions

As administrator of the RFS program, the EPA is responsible for identifying renewable fuel production pathways and pathway components that can be used in producing qualifying renewable fuel under the RFS program. The EPA is also responsible for announcing the RFS mandate levels for each year based on an evaluation and determination of the estimated production capacity (both domestic and international) of the various biofuels types. If it appears that the production capacity will be insufficient for a particular biofuel category—e.g., cellulosic biofuels—then EPA may announce a waiver of the original statutory RFS mandate for that category (and possibly other nested categories) to a reduced level. In addition, EPA may entertain RFS waiver petitions regarding potential economic hardship related to meeting a particular RFS mandate category.

Table 5. Selected Biofuels-Related Bills in the 113th Congress

Bill Number	Bill Name	Sponsor	Action
H.R. 550 S. 251	Phantom Fuel Reform Act of 2013	Rep. Gregg Harper Sen. Flake	To amend the RFS to require the cellulosic biofuel requirement to be based on actual production for the Jan.-Oct. period of the preceding year, pro-rated to an annual basis.
H.R. 596	Public Lands Renewable Energy Development Act of 2013	Rep. Paul Gosar	To promote the development of renewable energy on public lands.
H.R. 796	Amendment to the Clean Air Act	Rep. Sensenbrenner	To limit the cellulosic RFS mandate to be not more than 5% or 1 million gallons (whichever is greater) more than the total volume of cellulosic biofuel that was commercially available for the most recent calendar year.
H.R. 875	untitled	Rep. Sensenbrenner	To provide for a comprehensive assessment of the scientific and technical research on the implications of the use of mid-level ethanol blends (e.g., E15).
H.R. 979	Forest Products Fairness Act of 2013	Rep. Thompson	To modify the definition of the term `biobased product' to more broadly include forest products.
H.R. 1214	Domestic Fuels Protection Act of 2013	Rep. Shimkus	To provide liability protection for claims based on the design, manufacture, sale, offer for sale, introduction into commerce, or use of certain fuels and fuel additives (e.g., E15).

Bill Number	Bill Name	Sponsor	Action
H.R. 1273	Rural Energy Improvement Act	Rep. Welch	To reauthorize and improve the Rural Energy for America Program (REAP).
H.R. 1461	RFS Elimination Act	Rep. Goodlatte	To repeal the RFS program of the EPA.
H.R. 1462 S. 344	RFS Reform Act of 2013	Rep. Goodlatte Sen. Wicker	To prohibit the EPA from approving the introduction into commerce of gasoline that contains greater than 10%-volume ethanol
H.R. 1469	Leave Ethanol Volumes at Existing Levels (LEVEL) Act	Rep. Burgess	To limit expansion of RFS biofuel mandates, to prohibit authorization of ethanol blends greater than 10%.
H.R. 1482	RFS Amendments Act	Rep. Womak	To eliminate corn ethanol requirements under the RFS program
S. 289	Freedom Fuels Act of 2013	Sen. Baucus	To authorize long-term contracts for the procurement of certain liquid transportation fuels for the Dept. of Defense

Source: Legislative Information System of the U.S. Congress.

Notes: This is not meant to serve as a comprehensive list of all energy-related bills, but instead represents a selection of bills deemed (by CRS) most relevant to federal biofuels programs and policies.

Waiver of Mandated Use Requirements

The RFS mandates the use of over 16.55 bgals of biofuels in 2013. The mandate grows to 20.5 bgals of biofuels use by 2015. By 2022, 36 bgals of biofuels must be consumed under the RFS. Each year EPA must review the likelihood of outyear biofuel production meeting or failing to meet required RFS usage levels, and adjust the mandates accordingly. EPA's biofuels standards for each upcoming year are announced on a preliminary basis in the spring of the preceding year, when EPA issues a notice of proposed rulemaking, and on a final basis by November 30 of the preceding year, when EPA issues a final rule.[92]

The EPA has already waived the original RFS2 mandate for cellulosic biofuels for each of the first three years (2010, 2011, and 2012) and has proposed waiving it for a fourth year (2013). The likelihood of future EPA waivers could deter capital investments in the sector and make future waivers become a self-fulfilling prophecy. The likelihood of meeting RFS mandates for traditional biofuels hinges both on the "blend wall" and on the slow emergence of a national infrastructure needed to facilitate the distribution and use of the growing mandated biofuel volumes. Even if the expansion of the blending ratio to 15% for model year 2001 and newer passenger vehicles were to actually occur (presently an unlikely prospect due to infrastructure limitations mentioned earlier), the higher blend wall of approximately 20 to 21 bgals would become a real barrier to expanded biofuels use by 2015.

Estimation of GHG Emission Reductions

Under EISA, EPA is responsible for evaluating whether a renewable fuel meets the specific GHG reduction threshold assigned to its RFS category. Determining compliance with the thresholds requires a comprehensive evaluation of renewable fuels on the basis of their lifecycle emissions.[93] The concept of "lifecycle emissions" encompasses an evaluation of GHG emissions along the entire pathway of a biofuel from the production, harvesting, and marketing of its feedstocks to the processing and distribution of the biofuel, including any significant indirect emissions such as emissions from land uses changes that might result from changes in crop patterns due to the various biofuels incentives (as explicitly required in Section 201, P.L. 110-140).

More specifically, some have expressed a concern that expanded field crop production in the United States for ethanol production has led to commodity price increases that, in turn, have induced increased land cultivation in other countries, and as a result, have increased net global GHG emissions.[94] The measurement of indirect land use changes (ILUC) is necessarily inexact many potential activities and countervailing forces are involved. As a result, inclusion of ILUC as part of the EPA's lifecycle GHG reduction analysis has been controversial.

Initially, EPA's lifecycle GHG reduction models proved very sensitive to assumptions regarding the extent of indirect land use changes, and suggested that some standard biofuels may not be eligible for inclusion under the RFS. EPA models were updated prior to the final RFS rule (February 2009) using newer data and produced more inclusive results. For example, corn-starch ethanol was determined to achieve a 21% reduction in GHG emissions compared to the gasoline 2005 baseline, thus just surpassing the 20% reduction threshold.[95] EPA models for estimating land use changes and other life-cycle factors involved in GHG emissions are continually re-evaluated as new or better data, methods, or analytical techniques become available. The nature of the future changes to EPA models, and their potential to include or exclude certain biofuels, remains a critical aspect of the RFS mandates and the U.S. biofuels industry's ability to meet the mandates.

Endangerment Findings for Greenhouse Gases (GHGs)

On April 2, 2007, in *Massachusetts v. EPA* (549 U.S. 497 (2007)), the U.S. Supreme Court determined that GHGs are air pollutants covered under Section 202(a) of the Clean Air Act. The Court held that EPA must determine whether or not emissions of GHGs from new motor vehicles cause or contribute to air pollution that may reasonably be anticipated to endanger public health or welfare, or whether the science is too uncertain to make a reasoned decision.[96] This court ruling allows EPA to regulate GHGs without further congressional action, and could bring into play the issue of indirect land use changes, given their alleged GHG emissions effects, which may put all ethanol production in question. On June 11, 2010, a Senate resolution (S.J.Res. 26) that would have blocked EPA from using the Clean Air Act to regulate GHGs was defeated (53-47).[97] Prior to the vote, on June 8, 2010, the White House had issued a statement saying that if S.J.Res. 26 reached the President's desk (i.e., passed both chambers of Congress), President Obama would veto it.

Other Pending or Emerging Biofuels Issues

CARB's LCFS Restriction on Midwestern Ethanol

In January 2007, then-Governor Schwarzenegger established a Low Carbon Fuels Standard (LCFS) by executive order for California.[98] The executive order directed the state's Secretary for Environmental Protection to coordinate the actions of the California Energy Commission, the California Air Resources Board (CARB), the University of California, and other agencies to develop protocols for measuring the "life-cycle carbon intensity" of transportation fuels.

Under the LCFS, CARB proposed reducing emissions of GHGs by lowering the carbon content of transportation fuels used in California. The LCFS established performance standards that fuel producers and importers must meet each year starting in 2011. Unlike the RFS, which groups biofuels into four categories, the LCFS evaluates each fuel on its own demonstrated level of lifecycle GHG emissions. The LCFS requires that biofuels demonstrate lower lifecycle GHG than the fossil fuels that they replace. For corn ethanol, carbon intensity is lowered by using natural gas instead of coal as a processing fuel, substituting biomass for natural gas or coal, and selling DDGS wet instead of dry.[99] For biodiesel and renewable diesel, carbon intensities can be lowered dramatically by using tallow or recycled cooking oils instead of soybean oil.

As part of its LCFS modeling effort, CARB includes an estimate of the indirect land use changes (ILUC) impact of grain-based ethanol. Largely because of the ILUC value assigned to corn-starch ethanol, most midwestern ethanol production did not qualify for use as a transportation fuel under California's LCFS.[100] This result has important implications for how or whether the federal RFS mandates can be met for the nation as a whole, since California is the largest state (39 million people), the largest consumer of gasoline (over 11% of national highway fuel use),[101] and a major ethanol consumer of approximately 1.5 billion gallons annually.[102]

The ILUC inclusion sparked considerable reaction from biofuel proponents because the measurement of indirect cross-country effects can be highly ambiguous.[103] In late 2010, CARB adopted a resolution to integrate the latest ILUC research into the LCFS regulation. On November 9, 2011, CARB published an updated list of CARB-approved biofuel production facilities that included 22 ethanol plants in Iowa, 21 plants in Nebraska, 12 plants in South Dakota, and 11 plants in Minnesota among the 111 newly added biofuel-plant pathways.[104] On November 26, 2012, CARB published a "Final Regulation Order" describing the LCFS compliance schedule and carbon intensity lookup table for various fuel pathways.[105]

On December 24, 2009, several ethanol groups (including RFA and Growth Energy) filed a lawsuit asserting that the California LCFS violated the U.S. Constitution by seeking to regulate farming and ethanol production practices in the United States under the "commerce clause," which leaves regulation of interstate commerce to the federal government.[106] On December 29, 2011, a U.S. district judge ruled that California's LCFS law did violate the U.S. Constitution's commerce clause and issued an injunction halting enforcement of California's LCFS. The judge ruled that CARB had failed to establish that there are no alternative methods to advance its goals of reducing GHG emissions to combat global warming. After an initial request for a stay of injunction by CARB was denied, a second request for a stay of injunction, while CARB appeals the original ruling, was filed with the Ninth District

Court of Appeals and was granted as of April 23, 2012, allowing CARB to continue enforcement of the LCFS until a ruling on the appeal is made.[107]

EU Anti-Dumping Charges Issued Against U.S. Ethanol Exports

U.S. ethanol exports surged to a record 1.2 billion gallons in 2011 (**Figure 7**), driven in part by blending wall limits, but also motivated in part by a sharp fall-off in Brazil's ethanol exports due to high international sugar prices and a below-average sugarcane harvest. The top three destinations for U.S. ethanol exports in 2011 were Brazil (33%), Canada (25%), and the European Union (EU) (24%)—all three of which had their own national biofuels usage mandates. Large U.S. ethanol exports are problematic for two reasons—first, they run counter to the often-cited policy goal of national energy security, and second, they may conflict with biofuels policy goals in other countries, leading to trade disputes.

EU policy has promoted renewable energy use, along with GHG reductions and energy conservation, for much of the past decade.[108] As a result, EU policy support has engendered a substantial domestic renewable energy industry. As part of a "Renewable Energy Directive" adopted by the European Parliament on December 17, 2008, the EU established a 20-20-20 plan that calls for a 20% reduction in GHG emissions compared to 1990 levels, a 20% increase in renewable energy use (with a 10% share specifically in the transport sector), and a 20% reduction in overall energy consumption. As part of the 20-20-20 plan, the EU also adopted a mandate for renewable content in transportation fuels of 5.75% in 2010, rising to 10% by 2020. On October 17, 2012, the EU revised its policy proposal to state that the use of food-based biofuels to meet the 10% renewable energy target in transportation fuels of the Renewable Energy Directive will be limited to 5%.[109]

After the surge of ethanol imports from the United States in 2011, an association of European ethanol producers, ePURE, claimed that the blending tax credit—the $0.45 per gallon incentive known as VEETC—then available to U.S. biofuels blenders represented a subsidy, and that the importation of "subsidized" U.S. ethanol was hurting EU biofuel producers. As a result ePURE requested an anti-dumping (AD) and countervailing duty (CVD) investigation.

On November 25, 2011, the EU initiated an investigation into whether U.S. exporters sold ethanol at unfair prices and were backed by subsidies in violation of international trade rules to the detriment of EU biofuels producers.[110] At issue is a European allegation that international ethanol traders were exporting E90 (90% ethanol blends) to Europe to take advantage of the EU's lower tariff on such blends as well as the tax incentive for ethanol blending in the United States. In response to the EU anti-dumping investigation, the Renewable Fuels Association (RFA)[111] pointed out that the ethanol tax credits (most of which expired on December 31, 2011) were not made available to U.S. ethanol producers, but "to gasoline blenders, marketers, and other end users."[112]

After a 15-month investigation into a number of U.S. ethanol producers, the EU concluded that U.S. domestic policies aiming to encourage clean energy constitute an illegal subsidy and lead to artificially low-priced imports being "dumped" on the EU market.[113] On February 28, 2013, the European Commission announced that it will impose a five-year anti-dumping duty of 9.5% on all imports of bioethanol from the United States into the 27-nation bloc. In 2009, when similar complaints were lodged against U.S. biodiesel exports, the EU imposed duties of 40% for a five- year period on biodiesel imports originating from the United States.[114]

In response, on April 29, 2013, a bipartisan group of U.S. senators asked the U.S. Trade Representative (USTR), Demetrios Marantis, to investigate the EU decision and consider the possibility of filing a World Trade Organization (WTO) challenge to the European Commission's decision.[115]

The potential implications of an ethanol trade dispute between United States and the EU are unclear. However, the imposition of an import tariff will likely limit U.S. ethanol exports to the EU. Given the emergence of the blend wall as a constraint on U.S. ethanol consumption, combined with relatively tight ethanol supplies on the world market (following two years of successive poor Brazilian sugar crops—2011 and 2012) and biofuels usage mandates in several major fuel consuming nations, the United States may seek international markets for surplus domestic supplies, thus keeping the issue in front of policymakers.

End Notes

[1] This excludes the costs of externalities (e.g., air pollution, environmental degradation, illness and disease, or indirect land use changes and market-price effects) linked to emissions associated with burning either fossil fuels or biofuels.

[2] For more details and a complete listing of federal biofuels programs and incentives, see CRS Report R42566, *Alternative Fuel and Advanced Vehicle Technology Incentives: A Summary of Federal Programs*.

[3] See the list of related CRS Reports available at the CRS website "Issues in Focus: Agriculture: Agriculture-Based Biofuels" including CRS Report R41985, *Renewable Energy Programs and the Farm Bill: Status and Issues*.

[4] See CRS Report R40529, *Biomass: Comparison of Definitions in Legislation Through the 112th Congress*.

[5] See CRS Report R40155, *Renewable Fuel Standard (RFS): Overview and Issues*.

[6] See CRS Report R42122, *Algae's Potential as a Transportation Biofuel*.

[7] According to data from the Renewable Fuel Association, U.S. ethanol production in 2012 was 13.3 billion gallons (61%), Brazil's was 5.8 billion gallons (27%), and the world total was 21.8 billion gallons (100%).

[8] In 2012, 20,069 gallons of cellulosic biofuels production were reported to the Environmental Protection Agency (EPA) under its RFS2 EMTS Informational Data system, at http://www.epa.gov/otaq/fuels/rfsdata/. Data concerning cellulosic biofuels production costs is proprietary and has not been made publicly available.

[9] See CRS Report R41106, *Meeting the Renewable Fuel Standard (RFS) Mandate for Cellulosic Biofuels: Questions and Answers*.

[10] Energy Information Agency (EIA), *Monthly Biodiesel Production Report*, U.S. Dept. of Energy (DOE), March 2013.

[11] The RFS referred to as RFS1 was begun by the Energy Policy Act of 2005 (§1501; P.L. 109-58). A greatly expanded RFS (referred to as RFS2) was established by the Energy Independence and Security Act of 2007 (EISA, §202, P.L. 110-140). For more information on the RFS, see CRS Report R40155, *Renewable Fuel Standard (RFS): Overview and Issues*; this is described in greater detail later in this report, in the section titled "Evolution of the U.S. Ethanol Sector."

[12] Each RFS biofuel category has an identifier code associated with it: D6 is for an unspecified renewable fuel, D5 is for an advanced biofuel, D4 is for biomass-based diesel, D3 is for cellulosic biofuel, and D7 is for cellulosic diesel.

[13] CRS Report R40460, *Calculation of Lifecycle Greenhouse Gas Emissions for the Renewable Fuel Standard (RFS)*.

[14] Ethanol's use as an additive for octane or oxygenate purposes occurs primarily at low blend levels of up to 5%, and is small relative to the growth in total usage of recent years. When ethanol is being added to enhance engine performance rather than as a fuel extender, it is a complement to gasoline and may potentially capture a price premium over standard gasoline.

[15] Because the RFS categories are nested, their values will include a premium to reflect a higher nesting. For example, corn ethanol only qualifies for the total renewable fuel category (D6). Ethanol from other feedstock qualifies for the more restrictive advanced biofuel category (D5) as well as the D6 category. Cellulosic ethanol also qualifies for the cellulosic biofuels category (D3) along with the D5 and D6 categories. Thus, as long as the RFS mandate is binding, a gallon of cellulosic ethanol will have inherently greater value than a gallon of advanced biofuel which itself has inherently greater value than a gallon of corn ethanol.

[16] Biodiesel qualifies for the biomass-based diesel (BBD) category (D4) which, by its nested nature, also qualifies for the advanced (D5) and total biofuel (D6) categories. If BBD is produced under a production process that uses cellulosic biomass as its originating feedstock, then it may be defined as cellulosic diesel (D7) and qualify for the nested cellulosic biofuels category (D3).

[17] RINs are discussed in more detail in CRS Report R40155, *Renewable Fuel Standard (RFS): Overview and Issues* and CRS Report R42824, *Analysis of Renewable Identification Numbers (RINs) in the Renewable Fuel Standard (RFS)*.

[18] The exception is cellulosic ethanol, whose RFS mandate was waived to lower levels by EPA in each of its first four years of existence (2010-2013).

[19] Scott Irwin and Darrel Good, "Freeze It—A Proposal for Implementing RFS2 through 2015" *farmdoc-Daily*, April 10, 2013.

[20] For a discussion of the blend wall and associated policy and market issues, see CRS Report R40155, *Renewable Fuel Standard (RFS): Overview and Issues*.

[21] "Ethanol Policy: Past, Present, and Future," by James A. Duffield, Irene M. Xiarchos, and Steve A. Halbrook, *South Dakota Law Review*, Fall 2008.

[22] USDA, Office of Energy Policy and New Uses, *The Energy Balance of Corn Ethanol: An Update*, AER-813, by Hosein Shapouri, James A. Duffield, and Michael Wang, July 2002.

[23] "Status and Impact of State MTBE Ban," Energy Information Administration (EIA), U.S. Dept. of Energy (DOE), revised March 27, 3003; available at http://www.eia.doe.gov/oiaf/servicerpt/mtbeban/.

[24] The 30 million gallon threshold was extended to 60 million gallons by the Energy Policy Act of 2005 (P.L. 109-58).

[25] The Bioenergy Program was initiated on August 12, 1999, by President Clinton's Executive Order 13134. On October 31, 2000, then-Secretary of Agriculture Glickman announced that, pursuant to the executive order, $300 million of Commodity Credit Corporation (CCC) funds ($150 million in both FY2001 and FY2002) would be made available to encourage expanded production of biofuels.

[26] The CCC is a U.S. government-owned and -operated corporation, created in 1933, with broad powers to support farm income and prices and to assist in the export of U.S. agricultural products. Toward this end, the CCC finances USDA's domestic farm commodity price and income support programs and certain export programs using its permanent authority to borrow up to $30 billion at any one time from the U.S. Treasury.

[27] The Bioenergy Program was phased out at the end of FY2006.

[28] "Status and Impact of State MTBE Ban," Energy Information Administration (EIA), U.S. Dept. of Energy (DOE), revised March 27, 3003; available at http://www.eia.doe.gov/oiaf/servicerpt/mtbeban/.

[29] Ibid.

[30] Based on CRS simulations of an ethanol dry mill spreadsheet model developed by D. Tiffany and V. Eidman in *Factors Associated with Success of Fuel Ethanol Producers*, Staff Paper P03-7, Dept of Applied Economics, University of Minnesota, August 2003. Note, nameplate capacity represents the capacity that the design engineers will warrant. In most cases, an efficiently run plant will operate in excess of its nameplate capacity.

[31] See CRS Report R40155, *Renewable Fuel Standard (RFS): Overview and Issues*.

[32] For more information about markets during this period, see CRS Report RL34474, *High Agricultural Commodity Prices: What Are the Issues?* See also, "What Is Driving Food Prices," by Philip C. Abbott, Christopher Hurt, and Wallace E. Tyner, Farm Foundation, July 2008; hereinafter referred to as Abbott et al., 2008.

[33] On June 23, 2008, the nearby futures contract for No. 2, yellow corn hit a then-record $7.65 per bushel on the Chicago Board of Trade. On July 7, 2008, the nearby futures contract for Crude Oil hit $147.27 per barrel at the New York Mercantile Exchange, while the nearby Brent Crude Oil contract hit $147.50 at the ICE Futures Europe exchange.

[34] Permanent Subcommittee on Investigations, U.S. Senate, *Wall Street and the Financial Crisis: Anatomy of a Financial Collapse*, Majority and Minority Staff Report, April 13, 2011.

[35] See CRS Report R41985, *Renewable Energy Programs and the Farm Bill: Status and Issues*.

[36] See the section "2008 Farm Bill Expiration" later in this report for details.

[37] EIA, DOE, "Petroleum Products Supplied by Type;" http://www.eia.gov/totalenergy/data/monthly/pdf/sec3_15.pdf.

[38] USDA, ERS, *Outlook for U.S. Agricultural Trade*, AES-72, November 30, 2011.

[39] For more information on this and other market factors, see CRS Report R41956, *U.S. Livestock and Poultry Feed Use and Availability: Background and Emerging Issues*.

[40] And to help satisfy California's Low Carbon Fuel Standard (LCFS) described later in this report.

[41] Based on official statistics from the International Trade Commission, Dept. of Commerce.

[42] Midpoint of a projected range of $4.20 to $5.00 per bushel, *World Agricultural Supply and Demand Estimates (WASDE)*, World Agricultural Outlook Board (WAOB), USDA, June 12, 2012.

[43] *WASDE*, WAOB, USDA, August 10, 2012.

[44] Informa projects that U.S. ethanol production will fall by nearly 550 million gallons to 2013, to a level of 12.8 billion gallons—Informa Economics, "Retail Gasoline Price Impact of Compliance with the Renewable Fuel Standard," whitepaper prepared for the Renewable Fuel Association, March 25, 2013.

[45] EIA, *Monthly Energy Review*, March 2013; at http://www.eia.gov/totalenergy/data/monthly/# renewable.

[46] RINs are 38-character numeric and alpha codes generated when a qualified renewable fuel is produced or imported that move through the supply chain with the renewable blendstock and are transferred to buyers, either with physical biofuel or separated from it, as a credit. RINs are the basic currency for compliance and trades in the Renewable Fuels Standard. In RIN trade, D6 RINs for ethanol and D4 RINs for biomass diesel or biodiesel get the most attention because they are the most liquid. For information on RINs, see CRS Report R40155, *Renewable Fuel Standard (RFS): Overview and Issues* and CRS Report R42824, *Analysis of Renewable Identification Numbers (RINs) in the Renewable Fuel Standard (RFS)*.

[47] OPIS Ethanol and Biodiesel Information Service, U.S. RINs (prices in U.S. $/RIN), Ethanol & Gasoline Component Spot Market Prices, various weekly issues, January-March 2013.

[48] Scott Irwin and Darrel Good, "Exploding Ethanol RINs Prices: What's the Story?," *FarmdocDaily*, Department of Agriculture and Consumer Economics, University of Illinois, March 8, 2013, at http://farmdocdaily.illinois.edu/.

[49] See CRS Report R40155, *Renewable Fuel Standard (RFS): Overview and Issues*.

[50] See CRS Report R40155, *Renewable Fuel Standard (RFS): Overview and Issues*.

[51] See CRS Report R41106, *Meeting the Renewable Fuel Standard (RFS) Mandate for Cellulosic Biofuels: Questions and Answers*.

[52] Cellulosic biofuels are derived from the sugar contained in plant cellulose. For more information, see CRS Report R41106, *Meeting the Renewable Fuel Standard (RFS) Mandate for Cellulosic Biofuels: Questions and Answers*.

[53] EIA, *Monthly Biodiesel Production Report*, DOE, March 2013.

[54] Robert Wisner, "Feedstocks Used for U.S. Biodiesel: How Important is Corn Oil?" *AgMRC Renewable Energy & Climate Change Newsletter*, April 2013, at http://www.agmrc.org.

[55] For more information, visit the NBB at http://www.biodiesel.org.

[56] EIA, DOE; biodiesel production estimates from "Annual Energy Outlook 2013," Transportation Sector Energy Use by Mode and Type, Reference Case.

[57] See section "The Ethanol Industry's Perfect Storm in 2005."

[58] While similar to "biodiesel," "renewable diesel" is produced through different processes and results in a fuel with somewhat different chemical characteristics. There is a separate tax credit of $1.00 per gallon for renewable diesel.

[59] DOE, EIA, *Monthly Biodiesel Production Report*, March 2009.

[60] EPA, "EPA Proposes 2013 Renewable Fuel Standards," EPA-420-F-13-007, January 2013.

[61] "EU Imposes Five-Year AD, CVD Duties on U.S. Biodiesel," *Inside U.S. Trade*, July 7, 2009.

[62] EIA, *Monthly Energy Review*, March 2013, Table 10.4 "Biodiesel Overview."

[63] "Tax Credits, Mandates Bring Back Biodiesel Plants," *Energy & Environmental New*, September 19, 2011.

[64] Robert Wisner, "Feedstocks Used for U.S. Biodiesel: How Important is Corn Oil?" *AgMRC Renewable Energy & Climate Change Newsletter*, April 2013; at http://www.agmrc.org.

[65] Federal Highway Administration, U.S. Deptartment of Transportation, "State Motor-Vehicle Registration—2011," March 2013, at http://www.fhwa.dot.gov/policyinformation/statistics/2011/pdf/mv1.pdf.

[66] Renewable Fuel Association, "E85," at http://www.ethanolrfa.org/pages/e-85.

[67] CRS Report R40445, *Intermediate-Level Blends of Ethanol in Gasoline, and the Ethanol "Blend Wall"*.

[68] Data is from EIA/DOE's 2013 Annual Energy Outlook. EIA also projects the U.S. national biodiesel transportation fuel market to show slow but steady growth (at about 1% per year) from about 47 bgals in 2012 to nearly 54 bgals by 2022. As a result, RFS BBD's share of the biodiesel transportation fuel market is projected to remain steady at about 2.5% through 2022.

[69] EPA, Fuels and Fuel Additives, "EPA Announces E15 Partial Waiver Decision and Fuel Pump Labeling Proposal," EPA420-F-10-054, October 13, 2010; at http://www.epa.gov/otaq/regs/fuels/additive/e15/420f10054.htm.

[70] See EPA, "E15 (a blend of gasoline and ethanol)," at http://www.epa.gov/otaq/regs/fuels/additive/e15/.

[71] For more information on potential misfueling, see CRS Report R40155, *Renewable Fuel Standard (RFS): Overview and Issues*

[72] "E15 Decision Opens Blend to 2 Out of 3 Vehicles; More Work Yet to be Done," RFA news release, Jan. 21, 2011.

[73] For more information, see the Renewable Fuels Association's E-85 online information site at http://www.ethanolrfa.org/pages/e-85.

[74] Based on CRS calculations using EIA and USDA data.

[75] Examples of ethanol policy proponents include the Renewable Fuels Association (RFA), the National Corn Growers Association (NCGA), and Growth Energy. Biodiesel proponents include the American Soybean Association and the National Biodiesel Board.

[76] Advocates of this position include free-market proponents such as the Cato Institute, federal budget watchdog groups such as Citizens Against Government Waste, Taxpayers for Common Sense, and farm subsidy watchdog groups such as the Environmental Working Group.

[77] For example, see James and Stephen Eaves, "Is Ethanol the 'Energy Security' Solution?" editorial, Washingtonpost.com, October 3, 2007; or R. Wisner and P. Baumel, "Ethanol, Exports, and Livestock: Will There be Enough Corn to Supply Future Needs?," *Feedstuffs*, no. 30, vol. 76, July 26, 2004.

[78] For example, the American Petroleum Institute (API) and the American Fuel & Petrochemical Manufacturers (AFPM) have brought legal challenges against certain aspects of federal biofuels programs.

[79] For a more complete list of federal biofuels incentives, see CRS Report R40110, *Biofuels Incentives: A Summary of Federal Programs*.

[80] See CRS Report RS21930, *Ethanol Imports and the Caribbean Basin Initiative (CBI)*.

[81] RFS (referred to as RFS1) was begun by the Energy Policy Act of 2005, (§ 1501; P.L. 109-58). The RFS was greatly expanded (referred to as RFS2) by the Energy Independence and Security Act of 2007 (EISA, § 202, P.L. 110-140). For more information on the RFS, see CRS Report R40155, *Renewable Fuel Standard (RFS): Overview and Issues*.

[82] See the earlier section, "The Renewable Fuel Standard (RFS)," for more details.

[83] CRS Report R40460, *Calculation of Lifecycle Greenhouse Gas Emissions for the Renewable Fuel Standard (RFS)*.

[84] CRS Report R41985, *Renewable Energy Programs and the Farm Bill: Status and Issues*.

[85] Originally the allowance was for cellulosic biofuel plant property. However, P.L. 112-240 amended the credit to included plant property used for non-cellulosic fuel produced from algae feedstocks. The special depreciation allowance involves 50% of the adjusted basis of a new cellulosic or algae-based biofuel plant in the year it is put in service, less any portion of the cost financed via tax-exempt bonds.

[86] For more information, see the "Federal & State Incentives & Laws," Alternative Fuels and Advanced Vehicles Data Center, Energy Efficiency and Renewable Energy (EERE), DOE, at http://www.afdc.energy.gov/afdc/laws/.

[87] For more information on U.S. farm programs, see CRS Report RL34594, *Farm Commodity Programs in the 2008 Farm Bill*; CRS Report R40422, *A 2008 Farm Bill Program Option: Average Crop Revenue Election (ACRE)*; CRS Report R40452, *A Whole-Farm Crop*

Disaster Program: Supplemental Revenue Assistance Payments (SURE); and CRS Report R40532, *Federal Crop Insurance: Background* .

[88] Mandatory funding is derived from authorizing legislation and is not subject to annual appropriations.

[89] For details see CRS Report R42442, *Expiration and Extension of the 2008 Farm Bill.*

[90] See CRS Report R41985, *Renewable Energy Programs and the Farm Bill: Status and Issues.*

[91] See CRS Report R41296, *Biomass Crop Assistance Program (BCAP): Status and Issues.*

[92] See CRS Report RS22870, *Waiver Authority Under the Renewable Fuel Standard (RFS).*

[93] For more information, see CRS Report R40460, *Calculation of Lifecycle Greenhouse Gas Emissions for the Renewable Fuel Standard (RFS).*

[94] Tim Searchinger et al., "Use of U.S. Croplands for Biofuels Increases Greenhouse Gases Through Emissions from Land-Use Change," *Science*, Vol. 319 no. 5867, February 29, 2008, pp. 1238-1240.

[95] "V. Lifecycle Analysis of Greenhouse Gas Emissions;" Regulation of Fuels and Fuel Additives: Changes to Renewable Fuel Standard Program; Final Rule, 40 CFR Part 80, *Federal Register*, March 26, 2010, p. 14786.

[96] For more information see "Endangerment and Cause or Contribute Findings for Greenhouse Gases under Section 202(a) of the Clean Air Act," EPA, at http://www.epa.gov/climatechange/endangerment.html.

[97] DTN Ag Policy Blog, "Senators Face Emissions Test," Chris Clayton, June 9, 2010.

[98] For more information, see "Low Carbon Fuel Standard," California Energy Commission, at http://www.energy.ca.gov/low_carbon_fuel_standard/index.html.

[99] EIA, "Biofuels Issues and Trends," October 2012, p. 25, at http://www.eia.gov.

[100] For more information see, "Proposed Regulation to Implement the Low Carbon Fuel Standard," Initial Statement of Reasons, Vol. 1, CARB, March 5, 2009, at http://www.arb.ca.gov/fuels/lcfs/lcfs.htm.

[101] Federal Highway Administration, Dept. of Transportation, "U.S. Motor Fule Use- 2011," Table MF-21, February 2013; at http://www.fhwa.dot.gov/policyinformation/statistics/2011/mf21.cfm.

[102] Todd Neeley, "US Scientists Demand Revision of Biofuels Carbon Accounting," DTN Ethanol blog, May 25, 2010.

[103] A 2010 analysis from Purdue University concluded that CARB overestimated the ILUC impact of grain-based ethanol by a factor of two in developing its LCFS: "New Study Undercuts California Low Carbon Fuel Standard, Shows Evolving Land Use Change Debate," Renewable Fuels Association (RFA), news entry, April 28, 2010, at http://www.ethanolrfa.org. The final version of the Purdue study was released as Wallace E. Tyner, Farzad Taheripour, Qianlai Zhuang, Dileep Birur, and Uris Baldos, *Land Use Changes and Consequent CO2 Emissions due to US Corn Ethanol Production: A Comprehensive Analysis*," Department of Agricultural Economics, Purdue University, July 2010, at http://www.transportation.anl.gov/pdfs/MC/625.PDF. Researchers at DOE's Oak Ridge National Laboratory (ORNL) concluded that ILUC resulting from expanded corn ethanol production over the past decade has likely been minimal to zero: RFA, "Dept. of Energy Researchers: ILUC Impact 'Minimal to Zero,'" 2010 press releases, October 20, 2010, at http://www.ethanolrfa.org; and Debo Oladosu and Keith Kline, ORNL, "Empirical Analysis of the Sources of Corn Used for Ethanol Production in the United States: 2001-2009," presentation to National Corn Growers Association, November 4, 2010; at http://www.ornl.gov/sci/besd/cbes/Symposia/Empirical_Analysis_Source_Corn_Ethanol_Nov2010.pdf.

[104] CARB, "Fuel Production Facilities with ARB Approved Physical Pathway Demonstrations," LCFS Program, November 9, 2012, at http://www.arb.ca.gov/fuels/lcfs/lcfs.htm.

[105] CARB, "Final Regulation Order (unofficial electronic version)," November 26, 2012, at http://www.arb.ca.gov/ fuels/lcfs/lcfs.htm.

[106] Todd Neely, "Court Strikes Down California LCFS: Ruling Opens Door to Large Ethanol Market," *DTN: The Progressive Farmer*, December 29, 2011.

[107] EIA, "Biofuels Issues and Trends," DOE, October 2012.

[108] European Commission, "Renewable Energy;" at http://ec.europa.eu/energy/renewables/.

[109] European Commission, "Renewable Energy/Targets by 2020;" at http://ec.europa.eu/energy/renewables/targets_en.htm.

[110] *World Trade Online*, "EU Launches AD, CVD Investigations into U.S. Ethanol Exports," December 8, 2011.

[111] The RFA is a U.S. ethanol

[112] "RFA Responds to EU Ethanol Investigation," RFA News Release, November 28, 2011; http://www.ethanolrfa.org.

[113] International Centre for Trade and Sustainable Development (ICTSD), "Disputes Roundup: Trade Remedies in the Spotlight in Geneva, Brussels," Bridges Weekly Trade News Digest, Vol. 17, No. 7, February 27, 2013.

[114] *Agri-Pulse*, "RFA Tells EU: 'It's Not Us!" November 30, 2011.

[115] Todd Neely, "Anti-Dumping Questioned," *DTN Progressive Farmer*, April 30, 2013.

In: The 2014 Farm Bill   ISBN: 978-1-63321-432-3
Editor: Wilmer Combs   © 2014 Nova Science Publishers, Inc.

Chapter 4

BIOMASS CROP ASSISTANCE PROGRAM (BCAP): STATUS AND ISSUES*

Randy Schnepf

SUMMARY

The Biomass Crop Assistance Program (BCAP) is designed to assist the bioenergy industry to overcome the hurdle of continuous biomass availability—viewed as a critical deterrent to private sector investment in the cellulosic biofuels industry. To accomplish this, BCAP is charged with two tasks: (1) to support the establishment and production of eligible crops for conversion to bioenergy in selected areas, and (2) to assist agricultural and forest land owners and operators with collection, harvest, storage, and transportation of eligible material for use in a biomass conversion facility.

BCAP was created in 2008 by the Food, Conservation, and Energy Act of 2008 (P.L. 110-246, 2008 farm bill). The 2014 farm bill (Agricultural Act of 2014; P.L. 113-79) extends BCAP through FY2018, with some modifications to its implementation.

BCAP is administered by the U.S. Department of Agriculture's (USDA's) Farm Service Agency (FSA). BCAP provides two categories of financial assistance: (1) annual and establishment payments that share in the cost of establishing and maintaining production of eligible biomass crops; and (2) matching payments that share in the cost of the collection,

---

* This is an edited, reformatted and augmented version of a Congressional Research Service publication, No. R41296, dated March 10, 2014.

harvest, storage, and transportation of biomass to an eligible biomass conversion facility. The payments have different eligibility and sign-up requirements, payment rates, and contract lengths. BCAP assistance for establishing and producing biomass crops is available within designated project areas. BCAP project areas are specific geographic areas where producers may enroll land into BCAP contracts and produce specified biomass crops. As of June 2012, eleven BCAP project areas had been approved.

Under the 2008 farm bill, BCAP was authorized to receive such sums as necessary, meaning that funding for BCAP was both mandatory through the Commodity Credit Corporation and open-ended since it depended on program participation. However, Congress—as part of the annual appropriations process—capped BCAP funding in FY2010, FY2011, and FY2012. In response to funding reductions, USDA temporarily suspended the CHST matching payment portion of the program through FY2011, and re-prioritized future program funds in favor of uses that emphasize annual and establishment payments, especially under existing contracts, over CHST matching payments.

Under the 2014 farm bill, BCAP is authorized with mandatory funding of $25 million for each of FY2014 through FY2018; no discretionary funding is authorized.

BCAP OVERVIEW

The Biomass Crop Assistance Program (BCAP) is intended to assist with some of the feedstock supply challenges facing the cellulosic biofuels industry. One ongoing hurdle for cellulosic biofuels development and manufacturing is the need for a constant supply of available biomass.[1] However, the cellulosic biofuels industry has struggled with the quintessential "chicken and egg" problem—investors are reluctant to invest in processing plants based on a technology (i.e., the conversion of cellulosic biomass to biofuels) that has yet to achieve success at a commercial scale, while producers are unwilling to devote land and resources to planting a dedicated biomass crop without nearby biofuels plants to buy it. In other words, the development of a cellulosic biofuels industry hinges simultaneously on the effective availability and use of new biomass feedstocks.

This report provides a description of BCAP's main components—annual & establishment payments, matching payments, and project areas—as outlined in USDA's final rule, along with a discussion of program funding and implementation issues.

Legislative Origins

Annual U.S. ethanol production expanded rapidly between 2001 and 2011, rising from under 2 billion gallons to over 13 billion gallons during that period.[2] To date, most biofuels production in the United States has been from corn starch. As a result, corn use for ethanol grew from a 7% share of the U.S. corn crop in 2001 to an estimated 40% share of the 2011 corn crop.[3] Dedicating an increasing share of the U.S. corn harvest to ethanol production evoked fears of unintended market and environmental consequences. As a result of these and other concerns, policymakers sought to redirect their bioenergy policies to provide incentives for the research and development of new agriculture-based renewable fuels, especially second-generation biofuels (based on nonfood crop biomass such as cellulose and algae), and to expand their distribution and use.[4]

In particular, through the Energy Independence and Security Act of 2007 (EISA, P.L. 110-140), Congress established a goal of 36 billion gallons of biofuel use by 2022, including 16 billion gallons of cellulosic biofuels.[5] Similarly, the 2008 farm bill (the Food, Conservation, and Energy Act of 2008, P.L. 110-246) included an energy title, Title IX, with a set of bioenergy programs administered primarily by the U.S. Department of Agriculture (USDA) that focused on non-cornethanol biofuels.[6] Among the Title IX bioenergy programs of the 2008 farm bill is BCAP[7]— authorized by Congress to support the establishment and production of eligible biomass crops for conversion to bioenergy in selected areas, and to assist agricultural and forest land owners and operators with collection, harvest, storage, and transportation (CHST) of eligible material for use in a biomass conversion facility.

The 2014 farm bill (Agricultural Act of 2014; P.L. 113-79) extends BCAP through FY2018 with some modifications to its implementation and with new mandatory funding, as discussed below.[8]

Program Operation

BCAP is administered by USDA's Farm Service Agency (FSA)[9] and receives mandatory funding through the Commodity Credit Corporation (CCC).[10] BCAP has two main statutory purposes: to support the establishment and production of eligible crops for conversion to bioenergy in selected areas; and to assist agricultural and forest land owners and operators with collection, harvest, storage, and transportation (CHST) of eligible material for use in a biomass conversation facility.

To meet the above-stated statutory purposes, BCAP provides financial assistance to owners and operators of agricultural land and non-industrial private forest land who wish to establish, produce, and deliver biomass feedstocks. BCAP provides two categories of financial assistance:[11]

1. **establishment and annual payments**,[12] including a one-time payment of up to 50% of the cost of establishment for perennial crops,[13] and annual payments (i.e., rental rates based on a set of criteria) of up to 5 years for non-woody and 15 years for woody perennial biomass crops; and

2. **CHST matching payments**, at a rate of $1 for each $1 per ton provided, up to $20 per ton, for a period of two years, which may be available to help eligible material owners with CHST of eligible material for use in a qualified biomass conversion facility.[14]

These two payments types—annual/establishment and matching—include different eligibility and sign-up requirements, payment rates, and contract lengths (**Table 1**).

Table 1. Differences Between Annual & Establishment Payments and CHST Matching Payments in the BCAP

	Annual & Establishment Payments	CHST Matching Payments
Location	Project areas only	Nationwide
Eligible Lands	Private lands	Federal, state, tribal, and private lands
Who participates	Eligible producers	Eligible biomass material owners
Contract vs. Agreement	Contract with producers; agreement with project area sponsors	Agreement with biomass conversion facilities; material owner must apply
Contract or agreement period	5 to 15 years	2 years
Payment type	Annual payments at the market rate plus incentives and payments for establishing the initial crop	Matching payment for the collection, harvest, storage, and transportation of eligible material
Payment limit[a]	50% of the cost to establish the crop	Up to $20 per ton matching payment

	Annual & Establishment Payments	CHST Matching Payments
Eligible for payments	Eligible Crop—crop of renewable biomass. Generally, crops that receive payments under Title I of the 2014 farm bill (e.g., corn, wheat, rice, and soybeans) and noxious weeds or invasive species are not eligible for annual payments	Eligible Material—renewable biomass harvested directly from the land, including residue from any crop that receives payments under Title I. Invasive and noxious species are considered eligible material. However, crops eligible to receive payments under Title I of the 2014 farm bill; animal waste and byproducts (including fats, oils, greases, and manure); food waste and yard waste; algae, bagasse, and woody eligible material collected or harvested outside of contract acreage that would otherwise be used for existing market products are not eligible.
Payment Reduction	Annual payments are reduced if crop is sold for any other purpose, including BCAP matching payments, or for contract violation.	Payments are reduced for contract violations.

Source: CRS and USDA, Commodity Credit Corporation, "Biomass Crop Assistance Program," Final Rule, 75 *Federal Register* 66212, October 27, 2010; and the Agricultural Act of 2014 (P.L. 113-79).

[a] Originally under the 2008 farm bill, establishment payments of up to 75% of the cost of establishment were available for perennial crops and CHST matching payments of up to $45 per ton were available for two-year period; however, the 2014 farm bill, §9010, lowered the establishment rate to 50% and the CHST matching payment to $20 per ton starting in FY2014.

Annual and Establishment Payments

BCAP's annual and establishment payments are available to certain producers who enter into contracts with USDA to produce eligible biomass crops on contract acres within designated BCAP project areas. They are intended to encourage longer-term investment by producers in dedicated biomass crops for bioenergy production.

Producer eligibility under BCAP's establishment and annual payments is limited to approved project areas.

Establishment Payments

BCAP establishment payments may cover up to 50% of the cost of establishing (i.e., clearing, planting, and seeding) a perennial crop, including woody biomass, within a project area. These costs may include the cost of seeds and stock for perennials; the cost of planting the perennial crop; and, for nonindustrial private forestlands, the cost of site preparation and tree planting. Previously established biomass crops, crops established using other federal sources, and annual crops are not eligible for establishment payments but may still be eligible for annual payments.

Annual Payments

BCAP annual payments would support up to 15 years of eligible woody crop production and 5 years of non-woody crop production. These payments would assist with the additional risk and possible forgone income associated with shifting away from traditional crop production. Annual payments are on a per-acre basis and would use market-based rental rates determined by FSA. Rental rate calculations are similar to those used for the Conservation Reserve Program (CRP).[15]

Annual payments may be reduced for several reasons, including

- if an eligible crop is delivered to the biomass conversion facility:
  - for conversion to cellulosic biofuels (payments reduced by 1% of the total sale price);
  - for conversion to advanced biofuels (payments reduced by 10% of total sale price); or
  - for conversion to heat, power, or biobased products (payments reduced by 25% of total sale price);
- if an eligible crop is used for purposes other than conversion to heat, power, biobased products, or advanced biofuels (payments reduced by 100% of the total sale price);
- if the producer receives a BCAP matching payment (payments reduced by 100% of the matching payment);
- if the producer violates a term of the contract; or
- under other circumstances determined by USDA.

Eligible Land

As defined in statute, only private agricultural and non-industrial private forest lands are considered eligible under the annual and establishment payment portion of BCAP. Federal and state-owned lands are ineligible. Lands enrolled in existing land retirement programs for conservation purposes—the Conservation Reserve Program (CRP) or the Agricultural Conservation Easement Program (ACEP)—also become eligible during the fiscal year that their land retirement contract expires. To address the concern of native grassland conversion, any land considered "native sod" as of June 18, 2008, (i.e., the date of enactment of the 2008 farm bill) is considered ineligible.[16]

Eligible Producer

Producers within the selected BCAP project area would be eligible to receive annual and establishment payments after entering into a BCAP contract. According to the USDA final rule, producers with already established eligible crops would be unable to collect an establishment payment but would remain eligible for annual payments. The project sponsor would also be eligible to collect annual and establishment payments, so long as the land is eligible and not federal, state, or government owned.

Eligible Crop

The 2008 farm bill defines the term "eligible crop" under the annual and establishment payment portion of BCAP as a crop of renewable biomass (see text box below).[17] This is different from the matching payment portion of BCAP, which includes a separate definition for "eligible material." Although both eligible crops and eligible material are defined as renewable biomass, exclusions for the two differ. Eligible crops under the annual and establishment payment portion of BCAP may not include crops eligible for payments under Title I of the 2008 farm bill[18] or any plant that is invasive or noxious or has the potential to become invasive or noxious. It is noteworthy that algae is included as an eligible crop, but not as an eligible material; thus, algae may qualify for annual and/or establishment payments but not matching payments, as described below.

Contract

BCAP contracts for annual and establishment payments vary in length: 5 years for non-woody perennial crops and 15 years for woody perennial crops. All contracts are required to have an active and current conservation plan or forest stewardship plan, depending on the type of crop grown. These plans seek to address environmental concerns of potential impact on soil, water, and related resources. Participants must also be in compliance with highly erodible and wetland conservation requirements.[19]

USDA-Sponsor Agreement

Agreements for annual and establishment payments may be made between USDA and a project area sponsor. Agreements specify the qualified project area sponsor's plans and how the sponsor will support the establishment and production of eligible crops for conversion to bioenergy in the BCAP project areas. This could include the type of biomass that will be used for the project, the intended use of the biomass and type of energy produced, and any new or proposed uses for the biomass.

Defining Renewable Biomass

The 2008 farm bill included a definition for renewable biomass under Title IX. This definition is retained intact by the 2014 farm bill. Accordingly, biomass has separate and distinct definitions on public and private lands.

Federal Lands includes National Forest System land, as defined in Section 11(a) of the Forest and Rangeland Renewable Resources Planning Act of 1974 (16 U.S.C. §1609), and public lands managed by the Bureau of Land Management, as defined in Section 103 of the Federal Land Policy and Management Act of 1976 (43 U.S.C. §1702). Biomass on public lands typically comes from tree and brush removal for fire prevention purposes, trees unsuitable for commercial harvest, invasive plant removal, and diseased, damaged, or immature tress culled in accordance with forest management practices. Thus in the case of federal lands, renewable biomass includes materials, pre-commercial thinnings, or invasive species that:

(1) are byproducts of preventive treatments that are removed to reduce hazardous fuels, to reduce or contain disease or insect infestation, or to restore ecosystem health;
(2) would not otherwise be used for higher-value products; and
(3) are harvested in accordance with applicable law and land management plans and the requirements for old-growth maintenance, restoration, and management direction, and large-tree retention.

Private Lands include nonfederal land or land belonging to an Indian or Indian tribe that is held in trust by the United States. Thus in the case of private land, renewable biomass is more broadly defined than when derived

---

from federal lands, and includes any organic matter that is available on a renewable or recurring basis, including:

(1) renewable plant material such as feed grains, other agricultural commodities, other plants and trees, and algae;
(2) waste material (crop residue, wood waste, wood residues, and other vegetative waste material);
(3) animal waste and byproducts such as fats, oils, greases, and manure; and
(4) food waste and yard waste.

For additional discussion on the definition of biomass, see CRS Report R40529, *Biomass: Comparison of Definitions in Legislation.*

CHST Matching Payments

CHST matching payments under BCAP assist agricultural and forest land owners and operators with collection, harvest, storage, and transportation of eligible material for use in a biomass conversion facility. Unlike the annual and establishment payments discussed above, the matching payments do not define eligible facilities by project areas.

BCAP's matching payments are available to eligible material owners who deliver eligible material to qualified biomass conversion facilities. They provide two-year contracts whereby USDA would pay—at the rate of up to $1 for each $1 per dry ton equivalent of biomass—the price to collect, harvest, store, and transport eligible material to biomass conversion facilities. Payments may not exceed $20 per ton.

Matching payments are intended to provide incentives for collecting underutilized biomass for bioenergy production. This would remove existing biomass where it might not currently be profitable to do so (e.g., crop residue or forest undergrowth). Eligible material must be harvested directly from the land and separate from a higher-value product (e.g., Title I crops). Invasive and noxious species are considered eligible material and land ownership (private, state, federal, etc.) is not a limiting factor to receive matching payments.

Conversion Facilities

A biomass conversion facility is defined in statute as a facility that converts or proposes to convert renewable biomass into heat, power, biobased products, or advanced biofuels. To become a BCAP qualified biomass conversion facility, the facility must enter into an agreement with USDA within the state where it is located.[20]

Eligible Land

Unlike under the BCAP annual and establishment payments, land is not a limiting factor. If the material is determined to be eligible, then the land from which it comes is not an issue. According to the USDA final rule, eligible material may be harvested or collected from certain National Forest System and Bureau of Land Management lands; from nonfederal lands, including state and locally held government lands; and from tribal lands held in trust by the federal government.[21]

Material Owner

A material owner must first apply and be approved as eligible by FSA before deliveries to qualified biomass conversion facilities are eligible for matching payments. For materials collected on private lands, an eligible material owner could be the landowner, the operator or producer of the farming operation, a biomass conversion facility that owns or operates eligible land, or a person designated by the landowner. For public lands, material owners must have the right to harvest or collect material through a permit, contract, or agreement with the appropriate agency or government entity. Federal government entities are not eligible.

Eligible Material

Similar to eligible crops under the annual and establishment payments, eligible material is also defined as renewable biomass. However, the exclusions to renewable biomass differ for eligible materials as compared with eligible crops. Eligible material does not include crops eligible to receive payments under Title I of the 2014 farm bill; animal waste and byproducts (including fats, oils, greases, and manure); food waste and yard waste; algae; and bagasse. Also, any woody eligible material collected or harvested outside of the contract acreage that would otherwise be used for existing market products is ineligible—this provision was added to prevent BCAP matching payments from pulling resources away from existing industries such as particle-board producers that often rely on low-cost scraps from construction zones and lumber yards.

In contrast, invasive and noxious species are considered eligible material. According to the final rule, eligible material must be collected directly from the land, separated from a high-valued product (such as a Title I crop), and collected according to an approved conservation plan, forest stewardship plan, or equivalent plan. This requirement is intended to prevent high-value products from becoming eligible for matching payments.

USDA—Biomass Conversion Facility Agreement

Agreements for matching payments may be made between USDA and an eligible biomass conversion facility. According to USDA's final rule, these agreements include items such as the obligations of the facility to provide a purchase list, receipts, and scale tickets for the eligible material owners; maintain accurate records of all eligible material purchases; calculate the dry ton weight equivalent of tonnage delivered; pay fair market value for eligible material regardless of the material owner's eligibility for BCAP matching payments; and make the facility's address and contact information publicly available.

Payment

Eligible material owners must notify FSA following delivery to an eligible biomass conversion facility. Once delivery is verified by FSA, payments are made based on total actual tonnage delivered, total payment received, and certification from the conversion facility. BCAP matching payments are limited to $1 per dry ton equivalent provided by the biomass conversion facility, not to exceed $20 per ton. Payment terms are limited to no more than two years beginning on the date of first payment by USDA.

Project Areas

BCAP assistance for establishing and producing biomass crops is available within designated project areas. BCAP project areas are specific geographic areas where producers may enroll land into BCAP contracts and produce specified biomass crops.[22] Participants may be eligible to receive financial and technical assistance as well as annual payments to establish these crops.

Project areas are established based on proposals submitted (on a voluntary basis) to USDA's Farm Service Agency (FSA) by either a group of producers or an entity that converts biomass to heat, power, a biobased product, or an advanced biofuel. The USDA final rule (75 *Federal Register* 66212) makes no restrictions on who may sponsor a project. Sponsors could include biomass conversion facility owners, such as federal entities, private entities, state or local government agencies, schools, or nongovernment organizations. Those interested in submitting a proposal are encouraged to contact their FSA state office for details. Upon designation of a project area, certain producers within the project area are then eligible to enroll land into the program.

The statute authority requires project area sponsors to include the following as part of the proposal:[23]

- a description of the eligible land including the geographic boundary describing the area where land can be enrolled;
- a list of eligible crops of each producer that will participate in the proposed project area;
- a letter of commitment from a biomass conversion facility that the facility will use the eligible crops intended to be produced in the project area;
- evidence that the biomass conversion facility has sufficient equity available, if the facility is not operational at the time the proposal is submitted; and
- any other appropriate information about the biomass conversion facility that gives reasonable assurance that the plant will be in operation by the time eligible crops are ready for harvest.

Project area proposals are submitted to the applicable FSA state office for recommendation to the national office. If the project areas spans multiple states, the project proposals are submitted to the FSA state office where a majority of the project area land is located.[24] Proposals are evaluated on a set of statutorily defined criteria, including the volume of crops proposed to be produced; the volume of biomass from sources other than those grown on contract acres; the anticipated economic impact to the project area; the opportunity for local producers to participate in ownership of the facility; the impact on soil, water, and related resources; the variety of biomass production approaches within the project area; and the range of eligible crops among project areas. Proposals meeting these criteria would be considered eligible for BCAP as project areas.

Project proposals are accepted by FSA on a continuous basis and, if the project is approved, producers within the project area could be eligible for annual payments and establishment payments. Producers within a designated BCAP project area may apply to enroll land into the program and receive assistance to grow eligible biomass crops. Biomass must be established, produced, and harvested or collected according to an approved conservation, forest stewardship, or similar plan to ensure that soil, water, and other resource concerns are adequately addressed on the enrolled land.

As of this report, 11 BCAP project areas had been approved. The project areas and their approved eligible biomass crops are listed in **Table 2**.

Table 2. List of Approved BCAP Project Areas with Location and Feedstock

Project Area	Location	Eligible Feedstocks
1	Kansas and Missouri: 39 counties	Mixtures of perennial native grasses and forbs, such as Switchgrass, Big Bluestem, Illinois Bundleflower and Purple Prairie Clover. Additionally, existing suitable stands of native grasses, legumes and forbs (existing native grass stands can be located on expired CRP fields).
2	Arkansas: 8 counties	Giant Miscanthus rhizomes of the "Illinois Clone," a sterile cultivar of perennial miscanthus giganteus.
3	Missouri: 9 counties	Giant Miscanthus rhizomes of the "Illinois Clone," a sterile cultivar of perennial miscanthus giganteus.
4	Missouri: 7 counties	Giant Miscanthus rhizomes of the "Illinois Clone," a sterile cultivar of perennial miscanthus giganteus.
5	Ohio: 4 counties; and Pennsylvania: 3 counties	Giant Miscanthus rhizomes of the "Illinois Clone," a sterile cultivar of perennial miscanthus giganteus.
6	Oregon: 5 counties; and Washington: 1 county	Camelina
7	Kansas: 5 counties; and Oklahoma: 1 county	Perennial native grasses and forbs, e.g., Switchgrass, Big Bluestem, Illinois Bundleflower and Purple Prairie Clover.
8	California: 17 counties; Washington: 17 counties; and Montana: 56 counties	Camelina

Table 2. (Continued)

Project Area	Location	Eligible Feedstocks
9	Oregon: 1 county	Hybrid poplar trees
10	New York: 9 counties	Shrub willow
11	North Carolina: 11 counties	Switch grass and Freedom Giant Miscanthus

Source: Farm Service Agency (FSA), USDA, "BCAP Area Project Listing," at
   http://www.fsa.usda.gov/bcap.
Note: The list was completed in June 2012. No new project areas have been added
   since June 2012.

BCAP FUNDING STATUS

Funding under the 2008 Farm Bill

Under the 2008 farm bill, BCAP was authorized to receive "such sums as necessary" for each of the fiscal years 2008 through 2012. This mandatory funding is provided through the borrowing authority of USDA's Commodity Credit Corporation (CCC).[25] As a result, USDA could use a virtually unlimited amount of funding from the CCC to implement BCAP, until the program's authority expired on September 30, 2012. Because funding is mandatory and paid through CCC, no annual appropriations are required for BCAP. Instead, actual BCAP outlays were to depend on the number of participants and the extent of eligible biomass crops involved in the program. However, as BCAP implementation unrolled and outlays exceeded initial expectations, Congress placed spending caps on the program's mandatory funding authority via the annual appropriations process.

Through FY2012, nearly $900 million has been paid out to projects in 31 states. This is substantially more outlays than projected under the initial 2008 projections of program costs by the Congressional Budget Office (CBO). CBO had originally estimated that BCAP outlays would be a cumulative $36 million during the authority of the program (FY2008-FY2012) including outlays of $3 million for FY2009, $6 million in FY2010, $11 million in FY2011, and $16 million in FY2012.[26]

No outlays were made under BCAP in FY2008 since the program was not yet operating; however, program costs soon escalated. In FY2009, $243 million in outlays were incurred, mostly as the result of CHST matching payments to biomass materials that met the legal definition of qualifying materials but that were not intended for use in the production of second-generation biofuels. As a result, Congress became concerned about limiting this type of unintended outlays and, in 2010, limited BCAP funding to $552 million for FY2010 and $432 million for FY2011 (2010 Supplemental Appropriations Act; P.L. 111-212).[27] A year later, Congress further reduced BCAP funding for FY2011 to $112 million (Department of Defense and Full-Year Continuing Appropriations Act, 2011; P.L. 112-10). In response to the reduced funding levels, FSA suspended the CHST matching payment portion of the program through FY2011.[28]

In its final rule for the BCAP program,[29] USDA announced a re-prioritization of program funds that emphasized annual and establishment payments, especially under existing contracts, over CHST matching payments (see next section "BCAP Implementation Status" for details).

With respect to FY2012 funding, the President's FY2012 budget proposed to limit funding for CHST to $70 million. The remaining annual and establishment payment portion of BCAP would remain at such sums as necessary (SSAN). On June 16, 2011, the House passed an FY2012 appropriations bill (H.R. 2112) that would have eliminated all funding for BCAP for FY2012. In contrast, the Senate FY2012 spending bill left BCAP mandatory spending untouched. In the final FY2012 Agriculture appropriations act (P.L. 112-55), BCAP mandatory spending was limited to $17 million.

In its March 2011 baseline, CBO projected that BCAP would have projected outlays of $141 million in FY2011 and $248 million in FY2012.[30] A year later, in its March 2012 baseline, CBO projected BCAP outlays at $24 million in FY2011 and $19 million in FY2012.[31] Final CCC outlays on BCAP for FY2012 were $15.9 million.[32]

Interim Funding in FY2013

BCAP, along with most of the other major Title IX bioenergy programs—with the exception of the Feedstock Flexibility Program for Bioenergy Producers—expired at the end of FY2012 and lacked baseline funding going forward.[33] However, the American Taxpayer Relief Act of 2012 (ATRA; P.L. 112-240)—signed into law by President Obama on January 2, 2013—extended the 2008 farm bill (P.L. 110-246) through FY2013.[34] No new mandatory funding was included for BCAP under ATRA; instead, ATRA included discretionary funding of $20 million for BCAP authorized to be appropriated for FY2013.

Funding under the 2014 Farm Bill

The 2014 farm bill authorized mandatory funding of $25 million for each of FY2014 through FY2018; no discretionary funding is authorized. In its final score of the 2014 farm bill, CBO projected BCAP outlays at $99 million for the five-year period FY2014-FY2018.[35]

BCAP IMPLEMENTATION STATUS

Implementation under the 2008 Farm Bill

As stated earlier, BCAP is administered by USDA's Farm Service Agency (FSA).[36] FSA's BCAP website includes URL links to the "BCAP Handbook" and other program documents, the latest USDA BCAP notices and news releases, as well as current information on BCAP project areas. This section includes a brief chronology of BCAP rule development and program implementation.

On May 5, 2009, President Barack Obama issued a directive addressing a variety of advanced biofuel priorities. The presidential memorandum requested the Secretary of Agriculture to accelerate investment in and production of biofuels, and it specifically listed energy programs in the 2008 farm bill, including "guidance and support for collection, harvest, storage, and transportation (CHST) assistance for eligible materials for use in biomass conversion facilities."[37]

On June 11, 2009, USDA published a Notice of Funds Available (NOFA; 74 *Federal Register* 27767) to implement the CHST matching payments component of BCAP.[38] USDA's notice eventually raised concern about possible market competition between the CHST matching payments program and existing wood manufacturing industries.[39] The NOFA was terminated on February 3, 2010.

On February 8, 2010, USDA published a proposed rule for BCAP (75 *Fed. Reg.* 6264) suspending CHST program enrollment and proposing rules to implement the remainder of the BCAP program.[40]

On October 27, 2010, USDA issued the BCAP interim (i.e., final) rule (74 *Fed. Reg.* 27767) which implements the full BCAP program, including the annual and establishment payment component.[41] The interim (final) rule adopted many of the provisions outlined in the proposed rule, made further revisions, and responded to the more than 24,000 comments received on the proposed rule.

In response to funding reductions through the appropriations process, FSA suspended the CHST matching payments portion of the program through FY2011.[42] The last deadline for submitting project area proposals for annual and establishment payments was September 23, 2011.[43]

As of June 2012, USDA had selected 11 BCAP project areas and continued to enroll producers for annual and establishment payments. However, due to the reduced funding availability imposed by limitations on the availability of mandatory funding through the annual appropriations process (see above discussion), USDA published an interim rule on September 15, 2011 (76 *Fed. Reg.* 56949), amending the BCAP regulation to provide specifically for prioritizing limited program funds in favor of the "project area" portion of BCAP. The limited funding available for BCAP means that not all BCAP requests can be funded. The interim rule explicitly provides a priority for funding establishment and annual payments for project area activities because "such activities will produce the greatest long term good in BCAP by providing an ongoing supply of new biomass."[44] Under the interim rule, matching payments for CHST would only be funded if resources are available after funding all eligible project area applications. The interim rule also enables prioritization among project area proposals if eligible requests exceed available funding.

Among the remaining BCAP-related tasks of the 2008 farm bill, USDA was required to submit a report to the House and Senate Agriculture Committees on the dissemination of the best practice data and information gathered from participants receiving assistance under BCAP no later than four years after enactment of the 2008 farm bill (i.e., by June 18, 2012). This report was made available in February 2013.[45]

Changes to BCAP in 2014 Farm Bill

The 2014 farm bill extends BCAP through FY2018 and makes the following changes to its implementation.

- **Land Eligibility:** Enrolled land eligibility is expanded by including land under expiring CRP or ACEP easement contracts.
- **Eligible Material:** Residue from crops receiving Title I payments is included as eligible material, while exclusions are extended to any whole grain from a Title I crop, as well as bagasse and algae.
- **One-time establishment payments** are limited to no more than 50% of the cost of establishment (down from 75%), not to exceed $500 per acre or $750/acre for socially disadvantaged farmers or ranchers.
- **CHST matching payments** may not exceed $20 per dry ton (down from $45 per dry ton) and are available for a two-year period. In addition, CHST funding is now available for technical assistance. Not less than 10% or more than 50% of funding may be used for CHST.
- **New BCAP Report:** Not later than four years after enactment of the 2014 farm bill, USDA shall submit to the House and Senate Agriculture Committees another report on best practices from participants receiving assistance under BCAP.

SELECTED ISSUES

Initially BCAP's CHST matching payments raised questions and concerns about feedstock eligibility, sustainability, and the slow development of cellulosic biofuels. Some of these issues were addressed by the 2014 farm bill. They are briefly reviewed here for historical context.

Eligible Crops and Material

Defining what is considered an eligible material or eligible crop under BCAP became somewhat contentious during the early years of implementation. By 2010, concerns had surfaced about eligible material creating direct competition with existing uses through the CHST matching payments.[46] Others have expressed concerns about allowing certain fast-growing non-native plants to be included as eligible crops.[47] Below is an expanded discussion on issues related to eligible material and eligible crops.

Wood Residue Competition

In early 2010, after USDA's 2009 notice on CHST matching payments, some manufacturing and nursery industries that use wood shavings, wood chips, sawdust, and other wood "scraps" noticed an increase in price for their raw materials. This increase was linked, by some, to the CHST matching payments, which offered a federal payment match for the same materials if delivered to a qualified biomass conversion facility.[48] The CHST matching payment of up to $45 per ton created an incentive for material owners to sell to biomass facilities rather than to manufacturers that use the same raw materials for products such as composite panels, particle board, and fiberboard, or to nurseries and landscaping firms that use bark and wood chips for mulch.

Renewable biomass harvested from the National Forest System and other public land is subject to a statutory provision that prohibits material that would otherwise be used for higher-value products.[49] This prohibition, however, did not initially apply to renewable biomass harvested from private land. In USDA's initial proposed rule (February 8, 2010), such biomass remained eligible for CHST matching payments, largely because the 2008 farm bill (P.L. 110-246) did not specifically prohibit biomass that would have otherwise been used for higher-value products produced on private land. However, based on the initial reaction to the CHST matching payments, USDA expanded the public land restriction to private land as well. Therefore, all biomass material that would otherwise be used for higher-value products, from either public or private sources, is considered ineligible under USDA's final rule.

In an effort to enforce this division between higher-value products, in its final rule (October 27, 2010) USDA added the requirement that *"eligible material be directly harvested from the land"* in accordance with an approved conservation plan, forest stewardship plan, or equivalent plan; be separated from a higher-value product; and not be classified as a higher-value product by USDA. For example, wood chips are considered eligible material if they are collected directly from the land. Therefore, wood chips collected from delivered and processed trees after the trees are delivered to pulp and paper facilities do not qualify. However, wood chips created in the field from diseased trees for ease of transport to a biomass conversion facility are eligible for matching payments. Another example would be corn cobs as an eligible material. If corn cobs are separated from the higher-value product (i.e., corn kernels) in the field and the cobs are then collected as residue in accordance with a conservation plan and delivered to a conversion facility they are considered eligible for matching payment. If the corn cobs are collected at a vegetable processing facility after being delivered and separated from the higher-value product, they are not considered eligible. This is considered incidental to the normal marketing of the crop and not representative of the collection or harvesting of biomass that would not otherwise be collected.

While manufacturing industries that use wood residue offered the greatest opposition to CHST matching payments as published under the USDA notice, those in the lumber industry that were receiving higher prices also questioned the sustainability of the provision. Some in the biomass industry highlight the temporary nature of the CHST matching payments (maximum two years), and hope that future implementation will focus on the BCAP annual and establishment payments, which are longer-term.[50] As mentioned earlier, in its final rule for the BCAP program, USDA announced a re-prioritization of program funds that emphasized annual and establishment payments, especially under existing contracts, over CHST matching payments. In addition, the 2014 farm bill lowered the maximum CHST payment rate per ton to $20, in part, to further minimize any incentive or preference away from existing uses.

Others question USDA's ability to distinguish between high-value product material and renewable biomass material in the future, despite the language in the final rule requiring it to be harvested directly from the land. Some believe the fungibility of wood could continue to generate competition between wood-based product output and renewable energy production.[51] The 2014 farm bill explicitly addressed this issue in Section 9010, where the definition of "eligible material" in previous law was rewritten to include the following exclusion: "(vi) any woody eligible material collected or harvested outside contract acreage that would otherwise be used for existing market products."

Invasive and Noxious Species

Some have expressed concern that eligibility criteria for materials and crops under BCAP may conflict with practices aimed at limiting the introduction of invasive and noxious species. Others, including USDA, praise invasive and noxious species' inclusion in BCAP as an incentive to further eradication efforts.[52] The BCAP program provides separate definitions of eligible material and eligible crops. Eligible *crop* criteria apply to the annual and establishment payments portion of BCAP and eligible *material* criteria refer to BCAP's CHST matching payments. Invasive and noxious species are considered ineligible as crops for BCAP's annual and establishment payments, but are not excluded as eligible material under BCAP's CHST matching payments.

The inclusion of invasive and noxious species as eligible material has generated both concern and interest in the environmental community.[53] Some note that while the incentive for removal is praiseworthy, such removal could have the unintended consequence of perpetuating the species. USDA's final rule addresses this concern by excluding removal and transportation during reproductive periods and requiring removal be in accordance with a new or amended conservation plan, forest stewardship plan, or equivalent plan. If a material owner violates the current federal standards for noxious weeds,[54] then all matching payments must be repaid. According to USDA, removal costs associated with spreading or establishing an invasive or noxious species while carrying out the activities to receive a matching payment are "outside the scope of BCAP" and would rely on state and other federal laws for penalties.[55]

Several plant traits of an ideal biomass crop are also commonly found among invasive grasses: low energy requirements for maintenance; efficient use of light, water, and nutrients; perennial growth; and high yields.[56] Based on comments received from USDA's proposed rule, crops of species such as giant miscanthus, pennycress, and black locust may be considered eligible energy crops. Many of these are non-native, fast-growing, perennial grass or trees that some consider an ideal energy crop for many of the reasons stated above.[57] Others are concerned that nonsterile varieties can become invasive and noxious[58] or that genetically engineered (GE) varieties could result in hybridization with wild relatives, resulting in invasive or noxious species causing economic and ecological damage.[59] Some states include varieties of these species on statewide noxious weed listings. In these states, they would be ineligible as a crop under USDA's final rule; however, there is continued concern that the plant's introduction as a crop could have unintended consequences, given that the USDA final rule does not distinguish between the sterile varieties and nonsterile varieties. Even the BCAP Final Programmatic Environmental Impact Statement (FPEIS)[60] highlights potential issues associated with the introduction of GE species and nonnative varieties for use as biomass crops. To prevent the spread of invasive or noxious species, USDA is relying on thorough, site-specific environmental evaluation of a project area prior to selection. This could potentially slow implementation of the program or impose costs on biomass producers.[61]

"Black Liquor"

In 2009, concerns emerged about "black liquor" meeting the definition of renewable material under BCAP, and thus potentially qualifying for CHST matching payments. Black liquor is a waste product from the paper production process composed of mostly organic lignin and inorganic pulping chemicals, and has long been used in the pulp and paper industry as a source of energy.[62] An existing alternative fuel excise tax credit targeting blends of biofuels with petroleum products for transportation purposes was expanded under the 2007 Energy Independence and Security Act (EISA; P.L. 110-140) to include alternative fuels used by non-transportation industries. As a result, paper companies, who were already using black liquor for processing energy at the treatment plant, by including a small mixture of diesel were now able to claim their black liquor as a biofuel that qualified for the biofuel excise tax credit. According to news reports, the black liquor loophole cost taxpayers over $4 billion in 2009.[63]

A provision in the enacted health care bill (P.L. 111-148) disqualified black liquor from eligibility as of January 1, 2010. USDA's final rule for BCAP states that black liquor is considered an industrial waste by-product and therefore is not eligible under BCAP. Despite this declaration, those in favor of black liquor's inclusion as an eligible source object to USDA's reasoning that black liquor is made from "inorganic" material, citing that "neither the statute nor the BCAP eligible materials list requires that eligible biomass actually originate directly from the land."[64]

The 2008 farm bill definition of "eligible material" simply referred to renewable biomass as: "(A) IN GENERAL.—The term 'eligible material means renewable biomass. The 2014 farm bill explicitly addressed this issue in Section 9010 by adding precision to the definition of "eligible material" as follows: "(A) IN GENERAL.—The term 'eligible material means renewable biomass harvested directly from the land ... "

Sustainability

BCAP has a dual purpose of establishing new dedicated biomass crops for bioenergy production (annual and establishment payments) and increasing the collection of existing and underutilized biomass for bioenergy production (matching payments). The latter purpose—incentives for biomass removal in areas where it is possible but not currently profitable—is a key factor for the forestry sector. The removal of hazardous wildfire fuels and invasive species could provide biomass for renewable energy conversion rather than being disposed of in ways that contribute additional carbon to the atmosphere.[65]

In addition to biomass removal from forestland, crop residue is also considered to be viable biomass for renewable energy production. Following harvest, the remaining plant, or residue, can be left on the ground for soil health, erosion and weed control, water quality, and nutrient management. The amount of residue left behind depends on the location, crop, and other locally driven factors. The research on crop residue removal varies in the amount that can be sustainably removed, ranging between 25% and 70%.[66] Many federal conservation programs provide financial assistance for practices that increase crop residue retention on the land, because of the environmental benefits.[67] The BCAP payments to remove this residue for bioenergy production have caused some to question whether this is a duplication of the federal effort and is counterproductive. Soil scientists in particular are concerned that the benefits to bioenergy would not outweigh the potential soil and environmental concerns associated with the removal of crop residue and caution against removing too much residue in sensitive areas.[68]

Dedicated biomass crops, such as switchgrass, hybrid poplars, and hybrid willows, are considered by many to be more desirable crops because they have a short rotation (re-grow quickly after each harvest) and use fewer resources, such as water and fertilizers, than traditional field crop production. Compared with field crops such as corn, dedicated biomass crops are also thought to have less impact on available food supplies.[69] Despite potential environmental benefits, concerns persist about the additional use of fertilizers and water resources that could be required to increase the per-acre yields to become economically feasible.[70]

Cellulosic Biofuels' Slow Development

The potential development of a cellulosic-based ethanol industry is presently impeded by the state of cellulosic conversion technology, which has been slow to move production from laboratory setting to commercial scale and which is thought to be expensive relative to corn-based production. In addition, U.S. ethanol production now appears to have hit the "blend wall"— the potential inability of the domestic market to absorb ethanol above a 10% share of domestic gasoline fuels.[71] However, the enormous potential supply of low-cost cellulosic plant material available in the United States makes it an attractive prospective feedstock and helps to explain its considerable policy interest.[72]

The 2014 farm bill energy title provides nearly $1.5 billion in financial incentives and support to encourage the production and use of advanced (mainly cellulosic) biofuels, including the $125 million in funding for BCAP.[73] Grants and loan guarantees leverage industry investments in new technologies and infrastructure, as well as in the production of cellulosic feedstocks. However, BCAP is the principal program designed to help "kick start" the U.S. cellulosic biofuels sector. BCAP attempts to remove some of the risk for biomass growers by supporting the production of dedicated crop and forest cellulosic feedstocks and by providing incentives for harvest and post-production storage and transport.

Despite support from BCAP and other federal programs, the cellulosic ethanol sector has been slow to develop. Currently, only small volumes of cellulosic ethanol are produced on a commercial scale. Only a few small refineries (mostly pilot or demonstration in scope) are engaged in limited production. Due to the slow progress in cellulosic ethanol production, EPA has been compelled to substantially reduce the cellulosic biofuel RFS mandates set by Congress for the years 2010 through 2014.[74] The EPA waiver of the cellulosic biofuels RFS for five consecutive years, coupled with reduced BCAP funding under the 2014 farm bill, and the congressional climate of budget austerity, likely increase the uncertainty associated with the future investments needed to kick start this sector.[75]

End Notes

[1] See CRS Report R41106, Meeting the Renewable Fuel Standard (RFS) Mandate for Cellulosic Biofuels: Questions and Answers.

[2] U.S. ethanol production has since leveled off at around 13 billion gallons. For a discussion of the rapid growth of the U.S. biofuels sector, see CRS Report R41282, Agriculture-Based Biofuels: Overview and Emerging Issues.

[3] USDA, World Agricultural Supply and Demand Estimates (WASDE) Report, February 10, 2014.

[4] See CRS Report R41282, Agriculture-Based Biofuels: Overview and Emerging Issues.

[5] See CRS Report R40155, Renewable Fuel Standard (RFS): Overview and Issues.

[6] See CRS Report R41985, Renewable Energy Programs and the Farm Bill: Status and Issues.

[7] BCAP is authorized by §9001 of the Food, Conservation, and Energy Act of 2008, which created a new §9011 within the Farm Security and Rural Investment Act of 2002 (P.L. 107-171; 7 U.S.C. §8111, et seq.).

[8] CRS Report R43076, The 2014 Farm Bill (P.L. 113-79): Summary and Side-by-Side.

[9] For additional BCAP information, see the Farm Service Agency's BCAP website, http://www.fsa.usda.gov/FSA/ webapp?area=home&subject=ener&topic=bcap.

[10] See footnote 25 for a description of the CCC.

[11] Farm Service Agency, USDA, "Biomass Crop Assistance Program (BCAP), "Fact Sheet," at http://www.fsa.usda.gov/Internet/FSA_File/bcap_update_may2011.pdf.

[12] Because annual payments and establishment payments have similar eligibility requirements and limitations they are discussed together and referred throughout this report as "annual and establishment payments."

[13] Originally under the 2008 farm bill, establishment payments of up to 75% of the cost of establishment were available for perennial crops; however, the 2014 farm bill, §9010, lowered the rate to 50% starting in FY2014.

[14] Originally under the 2008 farm bill, CHST matching payments of up to $45 per ton were available for two-year period; however, the 2014 farm bill, §9010, lowered the rate to $20 per ton starting in FY2014.

[15] For more information, see CRS Report RS21613, Conservation Reserve Program: Status and Current Issues.

[16] §9011(a)(5)(B)(ii) of the Farm Security and Rural Investment Act of 2002, (7 U.S.C. 8111 et seq.) as amended by §9001 the Food, Conservation, and Energy Act of 2008 (P.L. 110-246).

[17] For additional discussion about biomass definitions, see CRS Report R40529, Biomass: Comparison of Definitions in Legislation.

[18] As defined in the USDA final rule, these include whole grain derived from a crop of wheat, corn, grain sorghum, barley, oats, or rice; honey; mohair; oilseeds such as sunflower seed, rapeseed, canola, safflower, flaxseed, mustard seed, crambe, soybeans, and sesame seed; pulse crops such as dry peas, lentils, or small chickpeas; peanuts; sugar; dairy products; wool; and cotton boll fiber.

[19] Highly erodible lands compliance may be found under Subtitle B of Title XII of the Food Security Act of 1985 (16 U.S.C. 3811 et seq.) and wetlands compliance may be found under Subtitle C of Title XII of the Food Security Act of 1985 (16 U.S.C. 3821 et seq.).

[20] FSA makes the list of qualified biomass conversion facilities publicly available on its website: http://www.fsa.usda.gov/Internet/FSA_File/bcapfacilitieslist.pdf.

[21] Some restrictions do apply to the harvesting times, methods, and levels from nonprivate land.

[22] See FSA, USDA, "BCAP Project Area Information," at http://www.fsa.usda.gov/FSA /webapp?area=home&subject= ener&topic=bcap-pjt.

[23] §9011(c)(2) of the Food Security and Rural Investment Act of 2002 (7 U.S.C. 8111 et seq.), as amended.

[24] For more information, see "BCAP Project Area Proposal Guidelines," FSA, USDA, available at http://www.fsa.usda.gov/FSA/webapp?area=home&subject=ener&topic=bcap-pjt-bpro.

[25] The CCC is the funding mechanism for the mandatory payments that are administered by various agencies of USDA, including all of the farm commodity price and income support programs and selected conservation programs. The CCC is a wholly owned government corporation that has the legal authority to borrow up to $30 billion at any one time from the U.S. Treasury (15 U.S.C. §714 et seq.). It repays most of the funds it borrows with appropriations within the annual Agriculture appropriations law, usually as an indefinite "such sums as necessary" appropriation. For more information on mandatory versus discretionary authorizations, see CRS Report R43110, Agriculture and Related Agencies: FY2014 Appropriations.

[26] CBO, "Food, Conservation, and Energy Act of 2008—Conference Agreement," March 2007 CBO baseline (modified to reflect subsequent enacted legislation), May 12, 2008.

[27] For more on these types of changes in mandatory program spending, see CRS Report R41245, Reductions in Mandatory Agriculture Program Spending. For more information on the 2010 supplemental, see CRS Report R41255, FY2010 Supplemental Appropriations for Agriculture.

[28] USDA, FSA, Prioritizing Limited BCAP Funds for Establishment of and Annual Payments for Approved Project Area Activities, Notice BCAP-27, Washington, DC, September 15, 2011, http://www.fsa.usda.gov/Internet/ FSA_Notice/bcap_27.pdf.

[29] Biomass Crop Assistance Program," Final Rule, 75 Federal Register 66212, October 27, 2010.

[30] CBO, "CBO March 2011 Baseline for CCC & FCIC," March 2011.

[31] CBO, "CBO March 2012 Baseline for CCC & FCIC," March 2012.

[32] USDA, 2014 Budget Explanatory Notes for Committee on Appropriations, Commodity Credit Corporation, Vol.2.

[33] See CRS Report R41433, Expiring Farm Bill Programs Without a Budget Baseline.

[34] See CRS Report R42442, Expiration and Extension of the 2008 Farm Bill.

[35] CBO, "CBO March 2012 Baseline for CCC & FCIC," March 2012.

[36] For additional BCAP information, see the Farm Service Agency's BCAP website at http://www.fsa.usda.gov/bcap.

[37] U.S. President (Obama), "Memorandum on Biofuels and Rural Economic Development," Daily Compilation of Presidential Documents, vol. DCPD200900328 (May 5, 2009).

[38] USDA, Commodity Credit Corporation (CCC), "Notice of Funds Availability (NOFA) for the Collection, Harvest, Storage, and Transportation of Eligible Material," 74 Federal Register 27767-27772, June 11, 2009.

[39] "CPA says USDA Biomass Program a Threat to Wood Products Industry," Wood and Wood Products, Trends and News, December 2009.

[40] USDA, CCC, "Biomass Crop Assistance Program," 75 Federal Register 6264, February 8, 2010.

[41] USDA, CCC, "Biomass Crop Assistance Program," 75 Federal Register 66201, October 27, 2010.

[42] USDA, FSA, Prioritizing Limited BCAP Funds for Establishment of an Annual Payments for Approved Project Area Activities, Notice BCAP-27, Washington, DC, September 15, 2011, http://www.fsa.usda.gov/Internet/FSA_Notice/ bcap_27.pdf.

[43] USDA, FSA, BCAP Funding and Project Proposal Submission and Review, Notice BCAP-22, Washington, DC, September 16, 2011, http://www.fsa.usda.gov/Internet /FSA_Notice /bcap_28.pdf.

[44] Federal Register, Vol. 76, No. 179, Thursday, September 15, 2011, p. 56949.

[45] FSA, USDA, BCAP: Biomass Crop Assistance Program: Energy Feedstocks From Farmers & Foresters," February 2013; available at https://www.fsa.usda.gov/Internet/FSA_ File/bcap_documentation.pdf

[46] U.S. Congress, House Committee on Agriculture, Subcommittee on Conservation, Credit, Energy, and Research, Representative Minnick's comments on BCAP, hearing, To review the implementation of the 2008 Farm Bill energy title, 111th Cong., 2nd sess., June 9, 2010.

[47] S. Raghu, R. C. Anderson, and C. C. Daehler et al., "Adding Biofuels to the Invasive Species Fire?," Science, September 22, 2006, p. 1742.

[48] Juliet Eilperin, "The Unintended Ripples from the Biomass Subsidy Program," The Washington Post, January 10, 2010, p. A03.

[49] Under Section 9001(12)(A)(ii) of the Farm Security and Rural Investment Act of 2002 (P.L. 107-171), as amended by §9001 of the Food, Conservation, and Energy Act of 2008, the term "renewable biomass" includes material that would not otherwise be used for higher-value products, if from National Forest System lands and public lands.

[50] Conference discussion at the Renewable Energy and Technology Conference, Washington, DC, February 4, 2010.

[51] Roger A. Sedjo, The Biomass Crop Assistance Program: Some Implications for the Forestry Industry, Resources for the Future, RFF DP 10-22, Washington, DC, March 2010.

[52] USDA, "Biomass Crop Assistance Program to Spur Production of Renewable Energy, Job Creation," press release, February 3, 2010, http://www.usda.gov/wps/portal/usda /usdahome?contentidonly=true&contentid=2010/02/0046.xml.

[53] Letter from Bruce Leopold, President, Wildlife Society, to Director of CEPD, USDA Farm Service Agency, April 9, 2010, http://joomla.wildlife.org/documents/BCAP_rule_comments.pdf.

[54] Executive Order 13112, "Invasive Species," 64 Federal Register 6183, February 3, 1999. Also see, CRS Report RL30123, Invasive Non-Native Species: Background and Issues for Congress.

[55] USDA, Commodity Credit Corporation, "Biomass Crop Assistance Program," 75 Federal Register 66222, October 27, 2010.

[56] Joseph M. DiTomaso, Jacob N. Barney, and Alison M. Fox, Biofuel Feedstocks: The Risk of Future Invasions, Council for Agricultural Science and Technology, CAST Commentary QTA2007-1, November 2007, http://www.castscience.org/websiteUploads/publication PDFs/ Biofuels%20Commentary%20Web%20version%20with%20color%20%20792 7146.pdf.

[57] Dan Burden, Miscanthus Profile, Agricultural Marketing Resource Center, August 2009, http://www.agmrc.org/commoditiesproducts/biomass/miscanthus_profile.cfm.

[58] USDA, NRCS National Plants Database, PLANTS Profile: Miscanthus Andersson Silvergrass, June 2010, http://plants.usda.gov/java/profile?symbol=MISCA.

[59] USDA, FSA, Biomass Crop Assistance Program Programmatic Environmental Impact Statement, Final, June 2010, pp. 4-52, http://www.fsa.usda.gov/Internet/FSA_File /bcapfinalpeis062510.pdf.

[60] Ibid.

[61] Jody M. Endres, Timothy A. Slating, and Christopher J. Miller, "The Biomass Crop Assistance Program: Orchestrating the Government's First Significant Step to Incentivize Biomass Production for Renewable Energy," Environmental Law Reporter, vol. 40 (2010), p. 10076.

[62] Bloomberg News, "Black Liquor Tax Boondoggle May Net Billions for Papermakers," by Bob Ivory and Christophe Doneville, April 17, 2009.

[63] New York Times, "Tax Loopholes Block Efforts to Close Gaping U.S. Deficit," by Jonathan Weisman, July 20, 2012; and Accuval, "Black Liquor Tax Credits: The End of a Loophole for the Pulp & Paper Industry," March 2010, at http://www.accuval.net.

[64] Letter from Paul Noe, Vice President for Public Policy at the American Forest and Paper Association, April 8, 2010.

[65] See CRS Report R40811, Wildfire Fuels and Fuel Reduction.

[66] Several research articles exist on this subject. An example of lower residue estimates is, H. Blanco-Canqui and R. Lal, "Corn Stover Removal for Expanded Uses Reduces Soil Fertility and Structural Stability," Journal of American Soil Science, vol. 73 (2009), pp. 418–426. An example of higher removal estimates is J. Sheehan, A. Aden, and K. Paustian et al., "Energy and Environmental Aspects of Using Corn Stover for Fuel Ethanol," Journal of Indian Ecology, vol. 7 (2004), pp. 117-146.

[67] For more information on available agricultural conservation programs, see CRS Report R40763, Agricultural Conservation: A Guide to Programs.

[68] Rattan Lal, "Is Crop Residue a Waste?" Journal of Soil and Water Conservation, vol. 59, no. 6 (Nov/Dec 2004), pp. 136A-139A.

[69] Bruce A. Babcock, Breaking the Link between Food and Biofuels, Briefing Paper 08-BP 53, July 2008, Center for Agricultural and Rural Development, Iowa State University, http://www.card.iastate.edu.

[70] Institute for Agriculture and Trade Policy, Growing a New Crop for a New Market, August 2009, http://www.iatp.org/iatp/publications.cfm?refid=106612.

[71] For a discussion, see CRS Report R40155, Renewable Fuel Standard (RFS): Overview and Issues

[72] See the section entitled "Potential Issues with the Expanded RFS" in CRS Report R40155, Renewable Fuel Standard (RFS): Overview and Issues; and see CRS Report R41106, Meeting the Renewable Fuel Standard (RFS) Mandate for Cellulosic Biofuels: Questions and Answers.

[73] Advanced biofuels include biofuels derived from cellulosic feedstocks; sugar and starch other than corn kernel-starch; waste material including crop residue, animal, plant, or food waste; diesel fuel produced from renewable biomass including vegetable oil and animal fat; butanol or other alcohols produced through the conversion of organic matter; and other fuels derived from cellulosic biomass. For more information, see details of Title IX in CRS Report R43076, The 2014 Farm Bill (P.L. 113-79): Summary and Side-by-Side.

[74] See CRS Report R40155, Renewable Fuel Standard (RFS): Overview and Issues.

[75] See CRS Report R41106, Meeting the Renewable Fuel Standard (RFS) Mandate for Cellulosic Biofuels: Questions and Answers.

INDEX

C

D

E

F

G

Q

R

S

T

Y